EV

Robert Wentworth was a world-famous film star and Laura Kent merely the nanny he had engaged to look after his little nephew; but that hadn't stopped her falling in love with him. But—'We don't have a tomorrow, Laura, you and I', he had told her firmly—so that was that. So just what right had Robert to object to her harmless friendship with Tony Graham?

THE DEVIL'S ADVOCATE

'Either your sister pays the price, or you do,' the implacable Julius Morrell told Luisa. And as the alternative was that her sister would probably go to prison, what else could Luisa do? Julius, she realised, had nursed thoughts of revenge for ten years. Now it was in his power, what would become of her?

THE FIRE AND THE ICE

Two years ago journalist Sara Ford had written a less than kind article about Max Christian—so when he arrived as the new-broom editor of the magazine she worked on, she feared the worst. And with reason . . .

THE DARK ONE

It could be said that the celebrated actor Laurence Martineau had been responsible for Katy's leaving her job at Metropolitan Television; at any rate, he had offered her a temporary job as his secretary. Hadn't she jumped out of the frying pan into the fire, though? For though he was not as disagreeable as her previous boss had been, he had a dark, brooding attraction that looked like being far more lethal . . .

EVER AFTER

BY

VANESSA JAMES

MILLS & BOON LIMITED
15–16 BROOK'S MEWS
LONDON W1A 1DR

First published 1983
Australian copyright 1983
Philippine copyright 1983
This edition 1983

© Vanessa James 1983

ISBN 0 263 74419 1

Set in Monophoto Times 9 on 9½ pt.
01–1283 – 73388

Made and printed in Great Britain by
Richard Clay (The Chaucer Press) Ltd,
Bungay, Suffolk

CHAPTER ONE

'LAURA! Laura! Come and find us . . .'

The children had insisted on going to the wood; she had allowed herself to be persuaded, and already she was regretting it. The light was fading fast, and it was cold. She stood there, stamping her feet to keep warm, wrapping her arms around herself, trying not to let them escape her view as they chased each other through the trees.

In a second they had both disappeared; there were giggles, then an eerie silence. Laura shook off her thoughts and hurried in the direction they had taken.

'Samantha! Jessy, come on out! We have to start back now . . .'

There was silence. Quickening her pace, she hurried to the edge of the clearing, peering round the trunks of the trees.

She paused, listening, waiting for the telltale, stifled laughter. They couldn't have gone far—why, only a second ago . . .

From here she could see through the trees to the fields beyond. The Warwickshire hills dipped and curved; in the hollow immediately below them the houses of the village were clustered together, as if for protection from the elements; in the thinning grey light she could just make out the shapes of roofs, see lighted windows.

'Samantha! Jessy!' Her own voice echoed through the trees, and she could hear the sudden sharpness of alarm in it. Forcing herself to be calm, she used her firm voice, her authoritative nursery voice, the one they had taught her at the training college. 'Stop this now! The game's over. We've got to go back . . .'

'Caught you!' There was shrill laughter, and two pairs of childish arms clutched at her skirts. Samantha gave such a bloodcurdling groan that she frightened herself, and Laura took the opportunity to grab both their hands firmly.

'Now, home!' she said, with mock sternness. 'And no more nonsense!'

'Did we *terrify* you, Laura? Jessy trotted beside her, looking up expectantly into her face.

'Absolutely.'

'Oh, good.' There was a pause. 'Sammy, do it again.'

Samantha waited until they were safely out of the shadows of the trees, then she groaned once more. She let go of Laura's hand and clumped down the path ahead, waving her arms.

'I am the ghost of Marston Court . . .' she intoned. 'I am the ghost of . . .'

'Marston Court?' Laura looked at her sharply, then across the fields towards the house she spoke of. 'Why Marston Court?'

Samantha took her hand again.

'Mummy says it's haunted,' she said complacently. 'There was a man killed in a d . . . what's the word?'

'A duel?'

'That's right. Years and years ago. Now he walks the corridors at midnight, he rattles his chains, and holds his side, like *this* . . .' She clutched her heart. 'That's where he was wounded, you know. And he *groans* . . .'

'Rubbish,' Laura said crisply. She glanced down at Jessica's face and saw her lip tremble, her eyes widen as she looked at her elder sister. How typical of Zara to tell them that sort of rubbish! she thought crossly.

'There's no such thing as ghosts, and you both know it. Now, let's see if we can walk back to the house in five minutes, shall we? Mrs Grove says there'll be crumpets for tea if you go to bed before the guests come tonight.'

Anticipation and greed diverted them, as she had hoped it might. Both cheered up visibly. They hastened along the road, past the drive to Marston, towards the village.

Laura talked animatedly as they went, and both children quickly seemed to forget all talk of ghosts and Marston Court. But underneath her chatter she could not shake off an irrational feeling of unease. As they turned off from the main road and down the lane that led to the Fieldings' large house, an odd melancholy possessed her. For a moment she wished she were going home. Then she shook off the thought, braced herself, as they turned into the drive. She didn't have a home, she told herself coldly. Not any more. And it was time she realised it.

As they reached the old rambling house with its wide porch, she fumbled for her keys. There was the sound of high heels, then the door was thrown back, just as Laura lifted her key to the lock. Zara Fielding stood silhouetted against the light, so it shone on the perfectly coiffed cap of bright blonde hair. She had spent the afternoon at the hairdresser's, and the hours had been repaid. She ushered her children into the hall with a quick impatient gesture.

'For God's sake, Laura,' she said irritably, 'I *told* you not to go far! There's a million things to do, you know, and I can't manage entirely on my own!'

Laura said nothing. Hardly on her own, she thought rebelliously. There was Mrs Grove to cook, Marie Christine, the *au pair*, to help out, and she herself had been pressganged into the arrangements as usual. All Zara had to do was spend the usual hour and a half getting ready before she wafted down the stairs to greet her guests with a perfectly timed entrance. Laura set her mouth and wearily began to help the two girls off with their coats and outdoor shoes. She had been on the go since six, when the baby Jonathan had demanded his first bottle.

'It's no good looking sulky, Laura!' Zara's voice was sharp. 'Ever since I got back it's been chaos! Jonathan woke up, and Marie Christine's no earthly good with him at all. Mrs Grove is behind as usual. None of the vegetables is done yet. Michael rang to say his train was going to be late . . .'

She paused for breath, and Laura felt her own despondency sharpen for a second at the mention of Michael Fielding's name. She knew what that meant; if he was late he'd have been drinking, and if he'd been drinking there might be a repetition of the kind of surreptitious overtures she had come to dread—the sly pats on the bottom, the arm apparently accidently brushed against her in a crude caress. Involuntarily she sighed, and Zara gave a little shriek of anger.

'You're getting mud *everywhere*! Now you'll have to sweep it up.' Her steely blue eyes glinted at Laura in dislike. 'You do *know* who's coming to dinner tonight, I suppose?'

'Yes,' Laura said shortly. 'You told me.'

In fact, she thought dully, Zara had spoken of nothing else for the past week, ever since she had pulled off what she obviously regarded as a considerable social *coup*. Robert Wentworth was coming to dinner. Others as well, of course, but he was the only one Zara Fielding cared about. Just because he was famous, she thought rebelliously. And rich. And handsome—if you could judge from his films, which you probably couldn't. If you liked men who looked as arrogant as the devil and as cold as an outcrop of granite. She'd

glimpsed him once, near the village, on one of his rare
appearances there, though glimpsed was hardly the word. He
had nearly knocked her over as he accelerated along the
narrow lanes in that horrible ostentatious car. He hadn't even
slowed; just a glimpse of the famous profile, of two tanned
hands on a steering wheel, a screech of tyres, then . . .

'Well, don't stand there dreaming!' Zara glared at her. 'If
you imagine he has a hall covered in mud at Marston, I don't.
Go and get the broom—and hurry up with the nursery tea,
please. Sammy and Jessy look exhausted. They should both
be in bed, shouldn't you, darlings?' She bestowed a
perfunctory kiss on their lowered heads, then looked at her
watch. 'I must go and change. They'll be here at eight. Oh,
and Laura . . .' Zara paused on the stairs, eyeing her
spitefully, 'Clarry has let me down at the last minute, so I
shall need you to help out at table tonight. I told Marie
Christine to put the usual things out in your room . . .'

'The usual things?' Laura stared at her. Zara had been
pleasant to her precisely once—at the interview when she had
first employed her—but even she had never taken things this
far before. She felt anger rise up inside her, and knew her
cheeks flushed. Their eyes met.

'Well, you know what Clarry usually wears—the black
dress, an apron. I can hardly have you waiting at my table in
a nursery nurse's uniform, can I?'

There was an icy silence. Laura turned quickly to the two
children.

'Sammy, Jessy, you go on to the kitchen and start tea. I'll
be in in a minute. Off you go!' Zara turned as they did, but
Laura stepped forward quickly.

'Mrs Fielding . . .'

The use of the surname brought her to a halt. The
suggestion that they should all use Christian names, as if they
were friends, as if there were no barriers between them, had
been made by Zara at that first interview, when she had
seemed so friendly, so warm. When Laura had been
completely taken in by her.

'Is there some problem?' Zara used a deliberately imperious
tone of voice.

'Yes, there is.' Laura paused. 'It was agreed, when I first
came here, I think the college made it quite clear . . . I am
supposed to be the children's nurse, and to be able to
concentrate on that.'

And it was stated quite specifically, she thought angrily, exactly what her duties should and should not be. They had been eroded ever since then, of course, but they most certainly did not include waiting at table for Zara Fielding's guests.

'As I recall . . .' Zara gave her an icy smile. 'As I recall, you are supposed to be helpful to the family at all times.'

'Yes, but . . .'

'It's up to you, of course. I wouldn't dream of demanding that you help me now. But I ought to remind you that you're still in your probationary year. There's still one month to go, and while you've done *quite* well up to now there's still my report to send to the college, isn't there?' Zara fixed her with an innocently wide-eyed gaze. 'You don't get your full N.N.E.B. diploma if that report's bad, do you, Laura?'

There was a short silence. Laura flirted with the attractive possibility of telling Zara Fielding to go to hell and take her report with her, and then rejected it. She sighed and looked away. It wasn't worth the battle; there was only one month left, though she'd never have stood it this long if it hadn't been for the children.

'Is that settled, then?'

Taking silence as assent, Zara turned on her heel, then paused.

'Oh,' she said, with a little smile, as if the thought had just occurred to her, 'Clarry's uniform will be a bit big, of course. But that won't matter, will it? You're not the kind of girl to harbour romantic ambitions for impressing my . . . guests, are you?'

There was the minutest of hesitations before the word 'guests', as if Zara might have substituted another word instead. Husband perhaps, Laura thought, and hoped she was wrong.

'Hardly,' she said quickly. Zara's eyes hardened.

'Not even Robert Wentworth? You see all his films.'

Laura felt the colour rise immediately to her cheeks again. 'Oh, I've encountered him in the flesh too,' she said quickly.

'What?' Zara turned back, her eyes suddenly avid. Laura gave her a sweet smile.

'Yes,' she said. 'He pushed me into a ditch, as it happens . . .' She waited until she reached the door to the kitchen regions before she finished the sentence, taking some pleasure in the confusion and annoyance on Zara's face.

'He was in his car at the time,' she finished, over her shoulder.

Zara's laugh of high-pitched relief echoed in her ears as she closed the green baize door firmly behind her.

The children had had their tea. Tired, and suddenly quarrelsome, obviously upset by the scene with their mother, they had squabbled over everything—the crumpets, the apportioned spoons of jam, the cakes, the temperature of their milk. When Marie Christine had taken them upstairs to run their bath, Laura gave Mrs Grove a smile of exhaustion. The older woman grinned, and refilled the huge brown tea-pot.

'I'd better get on . . .' Laura pushed her chair back tiredly.

'No, you won't, love. You have another cup of tea in peace for five minutes. You've been on the go all day, you have. And now there's all this tarradiddle.' She compressed her lips in a look of disapproval, and poured a cup of strong brown tea into Laura's cup. 'Such a carry-on! Anyone'd think we had royalty coming, the way she's fussing. Got you waiting on table, I hear?' She looked at her curiously, and Laura shrugged.

'I'm afraid so.'

'It's not right, though I says so. You ought to dig your heels in a bit, young lady. Tell her it's not your place. No more it isn't, either. You've got enough to do with them children mornin', noon and night.'

Laura laughed. 'Oh, why bother? It doesn't matter.'

'Used to,' Mrs Grove said darkly. 'Now, when I started in service, up at Marston—well, that was a *very* different kettle of fish, I can tell you. But that was old Mrs Wentworth, of course. An Honourable, she was. A proper lady, born and bred. Not like some as I could mention.'

Laura repressed a smile. This refrain was a fairly recurrent one, and if she didn't agree with Mrs. Grove's rural brand of snobbery, she agreed with the sentiments behind it. Zara Fielding might have pretensions; she lacked manners. Laura sipped her tea and smiled.

'Was that Robert Wentworth's mother?' she asked, partly out of curiosity, and partly to deflect Mrs Grove from the subject of their employer.

'Bless you, no. His grandmother, that was. I was only fifteen at the time. Trained me up, she did. All wasted now, of course.' She sighed. 'Turn in her grave, the old lady would now, knowing a Wentworth was an actor.'

'He's a good actor,' Laura said mischievously.

'I'll take your word for it, love. I wouldn't know, I don't

reckon films and such. All I know is the house'll go to rack
and ruin if it's up to him. Had it to himself near on a year
now, and not back more than twice in all that time . . .'

'Such a short time?' Laura looked at her in surprise. Zara
had boasted of the fact that Robert Wentworth was a 'near
neighbour', as she put it, from the week of her arrival. Laura
had assumed he had owned it for many years, however rare
his visits. Something about the house, its air of darkness and
brooding perhaps, seemed to suit him. She had, she realised,
instinctively bracketed the two together in her mind.

'Well, his brother ran it for him.' Mrs Grove looked
astonished at such ignorance. 'His younger brother—John,
that was. A lovelier man than that you couldn't wish for. A
kind word for everyone. Looked after the tenants. And him
with such a beautiful young wife. Came here once or twice,
she did—friends with her upstairs.' She paused. 'Tragic. I said
to my Albert, I did, at the time, it makes you wonder about
the justice of this world. It does really . . .' She paused, and
seeing Laura's look of incomprehension, pursed her lips. 'Out
in America it was—a car crash. Not long before you came
here. Killed instantly, they said, the both of them. The son
was saved, of course. After a fashion . . .'

She broke off, her face changing as she saw Laura's
expression. Instantly her eyes softened, and she reached her
hand across the table.

'Oh, I'm sorry, love. I was forgetting, running on like that.
Here, I've upset you, haven't I?'

'No—really. It's all right.' Laura stood up quickly. Mrs
Grove's plain kindly face watched her intently.

'Still fretting for him, love, are you?'

'Sometimes.' Laura shrugged hopelessly. 'It was so sudden,
you see. And when something reminds me . . .'

Mrs Grove stood up and put an arm round her shoulders.

'It's only natural,' she said gently. 'Right and proper. Why,
when my old dad died—well, Albert'll tell you.' She puased.
'Still, the heart mends, love, in its own good time. You'll see.'

'Yes . . . yes, I know.' Laura pressed her arm gratefully, and
gave her a reassuring smile. 'I'm fine—really.' She glanced at
the clock on the wall. 'I'd better get a move on. I've got to get
Jonathan's bottle, then there's his bath . . .'

. She turned to the kitchen door, and Mrs Grove patted her
shoulder.

'Run along, then,' she said gently. 'I'm sorry if I spoke out

of turn. But you remember what I said earlier.' She gave
Laura a broad wink. 'No kow-towing to her ladyship, you
draw the line, my girl. All right?'

'All right,' Laura said with a smile.

She thought about Mrs Grove's words, with the back of her
mind, when she went upstairs to the nursery. She had delayed
too long in the kitchen, and everything was chaos. Jonathan
had woken up again and was bawling lustily. Samantha and
Jessica, refreshed by their bath, were in high good humour
once more, and engaged in a pillow fight. Firmly Laura got
everything organised. When Samantha and Jessica were at last
in bed, she sat in the nursery with them, with Jonathan in her
arms, warm and soft, and smelling of talcum powder and
milk, and told them a story full of princes and princesses and
enchanted castles and fearful dragons. No ghosts, she
reminded herself sternly, as the two girls' eyes gradually grew
heavy, and in her arms Jonathan waved one pudgy fist in her
face in amiable contentment. It had begun to rain outside,
and beyond the curtains, beyond the safe circle of the
lamplight on the toys, and the two small beds with their
patchwork quilts, the wind hissed and moaned. Rain beat
against the glass, but it was far off, shut out; the nursery was
warm and peaceful.

'And then?' asked a small indignant voice.

Laura roused herself with a smile. 'And then the dark tower
fell down, and the dragon vanished. And he was never seen
again.'

'What about the prince and the princess?' Jessy fixed her
with impatient eyes. Laura rocked Jonathan gently; he was
falling asleep.

'What do you think happened?'

'The prince married the princess, of course,' said Jessy
scornfully.

'And they both lived happily ever after,' added Samantha
with a contented yawn.

Laura stood up carefully, keeping her voice low, so as not
to disturb the baby. 'You know the story already. Now, you
both wriggle down and cuddle your teddies. I'll be back in a
second.'

'Laura . . .' Samantha pulled at her skirt. 'You know in the
story . . .'

'Yes?'

'Do people live happily ever after? In real life?'

'Sometimes.' Laura gave her an extra kiss, and drew the blankets around her.

'Will Mummy and Daddy?'

Laura stiffened, wondering for a second if Samantha and Jessy had ever heard the ugly rows she could not avoid hearing almost nightly, even in this wing of the house. Samantha was seven; she decided quickly to lie.

'I'm sure they will, darling,' she said gently. 'Now off to sleep, there's a good girl.'

' 'Night . . .'

Laura switched off the lamp, lit the night-light, and tiptoed to the door.

'Laura . . .'

'What is it, Sammy?'

'I think you'd make a lovely princess. Like in the story. With skin like milk, and hair like . . . like a crow's wing.'

Laura laughed softly. 'A raven's,' she said gently. 'And my skin's just pale because we had a rotten summer and no sun. Now, off to sleep!'

Pausing outside in the corridor, she was relieved to hear the steady even breath of sleeping within a couple of minutes. She tucked Jonathan in his cot, on his side and not on his back, which gave him wind, then she tidied up the children's bathroom, and at last, feeling utterly exhausted, went along the corridor to the back of the house where she and Marie Christine had their rooms. As she pushed open the door of the small shabby sitting room Zara had allocated them, the clock struck seven.

'Whatever are you doing?' She stopped in astonishment.

Marie Christine was sitting in one of the old bulging armchairs in front of the gas fire, sewing industriously. On the floor in front of her was one ugly black serge dress. Across her plump lap, being neatly and expertly stitched, was another. Marie Christine looked up with a grin.

'This is yours.' She indicated the dress on the floor. 'And this is mine. *Voilà*!' As she spoke she knotted the thread, then bit off the end with her small white teeth. 'Don't look so surprised. I make a little tranformation here . . .'

'But that's our dresses for tonight!'

'I know this.' Marie Christine gave a complacent smile. Seeing Laura's puzzled face she clicked her tongue impatiently, and picked up the other dress, pulling Laura into the light, so she could see what had been done to it.

'It is ugly, no? It *was* ugly. But now . . .' She grinned. 'You
see? I lower the neck a little here. First I take off one button,
then—no, I take off two. I make a little tuck here, and *here*'.
She indicated the waist. 'Because you are so slim that I am
hating you. And then I take the hem, *so*, and I lift it up, two
inches, three maybe . . .'

Gradually Laura began to comprehend, and a smile came
to her lips.

'Zara will be *furious*,' she said wonderingly. Their eyes met,
and Marie Christine dissolved in giggles.

'But of course. But what can she do? *Il n'y a rien à faire* . . .
By the time we come in and she sees us, it is too late. Quick,
Laura, you must try this, then I can see how she fits now . . .'

Keeping their voices low, glancing occasionally and
surreptitiously towards the door, and periodically dissolving
into helpless laughter, they tried on the altered dresses.

'Now!' Marie Christine reached up, before Laura could
stop her, and pulled off the plain ribbon that held back her
hair, so it fell, full, heavy and loose, about her shoulders.
'Now, you look in your mirror, eh?' She dragged the giggling,
protesting Laura into their bedroom where, between the two
narrow and lumpy beds, there was an old faded looking-glass,
a full-length one, screwed on the drably painted wall.

'C'est incroyable, n'est-ce pas?'

It *was* incredible, Laura thought silently, all laughter
suddenly deserting her. Clearly Marie Christine possessed gifts
she had never expected. Somehow, by some magic of instinct
and some brilliance with a needle, she had managed to
convert what Laura remembered quite clearly as a perfectly
hideous dress into one of surprising chic—even, she thought,
blushing slightly at the image in the glass, of some eroticism.

The dress clung provocatively to her high rounded breasts,
to her tiny waist. The neckline now revealed the cleft of her
bosom, and the hemline stopped just at the knee, emphasising
the length of her slender legs, the delicacy of her ankles. She
stared at herself in disbelief, seeing a tall girl, with hair as
dark as the dress falling from a side parting straight to her
shoulders, with eyes almost as dark as her hair, fringed by
thick lashes. In the light her skin looked pale gold against the
black fabric. She stared at her own reflection in disbelief;
she'd been wearing her nursery uniform for so long now, and
her own clothes were all so shabby that she'd forgotten—if
she'd ever known—that she could look like this.

'And now, *la pièce de résistance*!' With a flourish Marie Christine produced something from a drawer. They were aprons, Laura saw. Not the long bibbed starched apron Clarry was forced into when she waited at Zara's dinner parties, but two small, frilled delicate concoctions of muslin that pinned low on the bosom, and tied in a full bow at the back of the waist.

'Where did you get *those*?' she asked, as Marie Christine, frowning intently, fixed them exactly in place.

'From Mrs Grove . . .' The French girl giggled again. 'She 'as 'ad them since she was—what do you say?—parlourmaid at this Marston Court. This afternoon when Zara is out she wash and starch them with me. It is for this the vegetables are not done . . .' She dissolved in laughter again, and began to sashay around the room, wiggling her bottom and hips in a ridiculous manner, so Laura had to laugh too. 'You see, we are like the French maids in a play now? You know? A little sexy, a little bit naughty. It will serve 'er right, eh? And when I serve 'im the mousse, this Monsieur Wentworth with the wonderful dark eyes, I shall look at 'im . . . like *this*. *Ça serait un coup de foudre*—how you say? When you love like a thunderclap, all at once, poof!' She clapped her hands dramatically together, and the two began to laugh unstoppably, till Laura could feel the tears start to her eyes.

'Stop!' she said eventually, holding her aching sides. 'Stop, Marie Christine, we can't . . .' She looked quickly at her watch. 'We'll have the leave the dresses as they are now, but we'd better wear the proper aprons—really. Zara will have forty fits!'

'So? I 'ope she 'as one 'undred. What do I care? And we cannot wear these other aprons.' Marie Christine gave Laura a cunning look.

'Why not?'

'Because today I have sent them to the laundry!'

There was a sudden silence, and the two stared at each other. In spite of herself, Laura felt a rising nervousness; only too well she knew Zara's capacity for making scenes. Marie Christine's face sobered, and she looked at Laura keenly, her eyes sharp in her wide, heavily boned humorous face.

'You see?' She spread her hands. 'I do this for me a little, because I 'ate 'er. But most for you. Because you are beautiful, Laura, and she cannot bear it. So, tonight, when she makes you do this, which is not your job, not my job, *parce qu'elle veut faire l'impression avec lui* . . . we 'ave a little revenge, *n'est-ce pas*?'

Laura hesitated a moment longer, foreseeing trouble, then suddenly she laughed. She'd been curbing her temper and repressing her tongue for so long now that the urge to be what she used once to be, before all this happened, before she came here, when she'd felt carefree and daring and sometimes—her father had said—decidedly wilful, was very strong.

She reached across and took Marie Christine's hand.

'O.K.,' she said quickly, 'you're on. And now we'd better go down the backstairs way, so nobody sees us.'

Still giggling, the two crept quietly down the uncarpeted back stairs, through the warren of pantries and wash-rooms and cupboards that lay at the back of the old house, and through them into the kitchen. When they came in Mrs Grove was alone, bent over the Aga stove. Hearing them, she straightened up, turned, and gaped. Gradually her broad face split into a delighted and conspiratorial grin.

'You look downright indecent,' she said warmly, 'the pair of you. And I couldn't be more pleased!'

'However many are coming to this thing?' Laura groaned, peeling the brussels sprouts.

'Twelve,' answered Mrs Grove shortly. 'And as far as *she's* concerned, one.'

No one needed to ask who that was, and Marie Christine giggled. Laura said nothing. She thought of the children upstairs in the nursery, and her cheeks burned with futile shame on their mother's behalf. She didn't understand any of it, she thought sadly. Why had Zara ever married Michael, who was both successful at his job, and fairly rich—but not successful or rich enough for his wife? Why had she had children, only to take no interest in them at all? And why, finally, had she agreed too cooped up in this house, lovely though it was, when all she yearned for was a place in London, and an endless succession of parties? Zara went to London as often as she could anyway; perhaps she met Robert Wentworth there, Laura thought suddenly. Certainly she knew him already—or so she said. Perhaps that explained his presence tonight . . .

'Oh, damn!' She gave a muttered exclamation. The sharp kitchen knife had slipped, and she had cut her finger. Mrs Grove gave it a quick look.

'Not too deep. Run it under the tap, love.'

She was right, but—irritatingly—the shallow nick refused to stop bleeding. Laura was still standing disconsolately at the sink, lost in thought, the icy water chilling her skin, while the bright blood dripped unstoppably on to the stainless steel, when the first guests began to arrive. She tensed inexplicably, listening for voices from the hall, but the passageway and the baize door muffled almost all sound. Marie Christine, less discreetly curious, eased back the kitchen shutters and peered out into the night.

'It is not 'im,' she announced definitely. ' 'E 'as a silver Mercedes. This is the boring old Ryders in their boring old Bentley.'

'Who else is coming?' Laura asked, suppressing her memory of that silver car.

Mrs. Grove rattled her saucepans disapprovingly on the stove.

'The best she could get round here.' She listed a few names of some of the more celebrated local residents—a retired novelist and his wife, a rear-admiral, a surgeon, the well-known correspondent of a London newspaper. 'Oh, and that Hugh Clancy, the one as opened that fancy restaurant over Snowshill way.'

'Still no Mercedes ...' Marie Christine still had her nose glued to the glass. 'It is gone eight. Maybe 'e does not come, eh?'

Laura turned off the tap.

'I'm just going upstairs,' she said. 'I'd better put a plaster on this, and I'll just look in and check on the children.'

Upstairs all was quiet. Laura quickly bound up the cut, looked in on the sleeping children, glanced nervously once more at her own pale reflection in the glass. Without much success she tried to adjust the neckline of her dress; already she was regretting this prank. However much she disliked Zara, there were probably reasons, she thought, for her malice and bad temper. It couldn't be easy, living with Michael, who drank too much, and made passes at other women ... She sighed, and moved to the window, easing the curtains to one side and peering out.

It had stopped raining; the moon was just rising, lighting the sky with a pale silvery haze. Then suddenly she tensed. As she looked she heard the hiss of tyres on wet gravel, and a long silver Mercedes rounded the bend of the drive. Oh God, she thought, he was here! Suddenly possessed by an inexplicable panic she started back for the stairs, and raced down them helter skelter, into the kitchen.

There she came to an abrupt halt. The warm room reverberated with tension. The door was shut, Mrs Grove and Marie Christine were standing by the wide deal table, and facing them, white with anger, was Zara. Even as Laura came into the room she could hear the voice pitched low, using language she had never heard on the lips of a woman. She stopped, staring.

Zara was wearing a dress of ice blue silk that exactly matched her eyes. Her mouth was a vivid slash of scarlet in her white face, and her long scarlet-lacquered nails were clenched into her palms. The heavy, sickly scent she always used—Patchouli–wafted across the kitchen. She was visibly shaking. Her own dress, Laura noted, in a second of dour detachment, was slit to the waist, the low neckline emphasised by a heavy roped necklace of gold and pearls.

'. . . you little bitch,' she heard. 'Who's responsible for this? Where did you get that apron? I . . .'

Suddenly Zara saw her, and stopped. For a second she just stared across the kitchen, saying nothing. Her mouth worked, but before she could speak the door behind her swung open and her husband ducked in quickly, looking distinctly harassed.

'Zara darling, Wentworth's here and . . .' He broke off, seeing her expression. 'Whatever's wrong? Can't you come and . . . Oh!' He had seen Laura, and his mouth dropped.

'It's you, isn't it? This was your idea?' Zara's voice rose in pitch, and her eyes flashed at Laura. She turned furiously to her husband. 'Don't stand there gaping like an idiot! Don't you see what's going on? This slut is trying to sabotage my dinner party, that's all! She'll make me a laughing stock . . . What the hell do you think you're doing?' She advanced on Laura. 'Acting in some cheap French farce? Oh, my God!'

For one moment Laura thought she was going to be struck across the face. Then, at the last minute, Zara swung round and turned on her husband.

'What am I going to do? They're not coming into my dining room dressed like that.' She swung back again. 'Mrs Grove will have to serve dinner, that's all.'

'I'm afraid that won't be possible, madam,' said Mrs Grove stolidly, in tones that made it perfectly clear she was adamant.

'There's a lot of last-minute finishing touches to be done. I couldn't be responsible for the success of the dinner if I wasn't in my kitchen.'

There was a brief silence, and Marie Christine smirked. Michael Fielding put a tentative hand on his wife's shoulders.

'Oh, come on, Zara,' he said easily. 'I think they look quite fetching.'

'I know what you think!' She shrugged his hand off angrily, and his mouth tightened.

'Well, Wentworth's waiting,' he said coldly. 'So I suggest you decide what you want to do quickly and come and entertain him. You invited him.'

There was another silence, and for a moment Laura saw uncertainty and anger fight for dominance in Zara's face.

'Very well.' Her mouth set in a hard line. 'You serve the dinner. Marie Christine will take the left-hand side of the table and Laura the right. You serve my guests from the left. You keep you mouths shut and spare me any further vulgarity. Then you get out of the room and stay out. And you can both come and see me first thing in the morning!'

She turned to her husband, who was still standing, gazing in frank admiration at Laura.

'Michael,' she said icily, 'if you can possible tear yourself away . . .'

As her husband held back the door for her, and she swung out through the short passageway into the hall, Laura saw just a glimpse of a dark dinner jacket, a tanned hand, that Zara instantly reached for.

'Robert, *darling* . . .' she heard.

Then the door swung shut.

CHAPTER TWO

'HOWEVER much longer before they go in?' Mrs Grove looked irritably at the clock. 'It's nearly nine now. Those pheasants were done half an hour ago, and they won't rest for ever. Good thing I didn't start on my soufflé! Though at this rate they'll be so legless they wouldn't know the difference . . .'

They finally heard the guests cross the hall, amidst much laughter, about ten minutes later. A couple of minutes after that Zara pressed the service bell. Mrs Grove rose briskly to her feet.

'Right,' she said, 'we're off and running. Now, no more larks, you two. A joke's a joke, and I liked this one, but we've had enough trouble in my kitchen for one evening . . .'

Suddenly feeling extremely nervous, Laura followed Marie Christine silently across the wide hall, and together they paused outside the heavy mahogany door that led into the dining room. From behind it came the sound of animated conversation. It was all very well for Marie Christine, Laura thought. She'd done this before, helping the stolid Clarry on numerous occasions. But she really had very little idea what to do. Supposing she did drop something? Nervously she adjusted the now skimpy dress once more; she felt an idiot, she decided.

But when they went into the room, her spirits lifted somewhat. Zara had reduced the lighting to the minimum; the only illumination came from the logs banked in the fireplace, and the flickering light of the candles that reflected in the polished surface of the table, on the silver, the pale china, the beautiful polished fruit.

In this lighting, and in dark dresses, she and Marie Christine were well nigh invisible. No one was paying them the slightest attention anyway, they were all too engrossed in conversation. Quickly Laura stationed herself by Marie Christine at the sideboard, and picked up one of the beautifully decorated bowls of salmon mousse. Fragments of conversation, casual endearments, bursts of laughter all tangled meaninglessly in her mind. The room blurred, and then, as she turned hesitantly it resolved itself, shifted, and focused.

One man was taking no part in the conversation around him. He was seated in the middle of the table, opposite her, and he was leaning slightly back in his chair, one arm draped casually over its back. He looked bored, and too arrogant to bother to hide it, and even though his features were so instantly familiar to her, their harsh beauty was startling. She saw him in the moment he saw her, and for a fraction of a second she paused. Between them a candle guttered and flared, throwing light on his face, throwing his eyes into shadow.

Then he moved, very slightly, so she could see his eyes, darkly blazing. She had a moment's confused impression: of an effortless, lazy magnetism, a contained power; also of a curious but total detachment, a solitariness. Then she realised his eyes were travelling lazily, almost mockingly, down from her face to her throat, to where her skin shone palely in the candlelight above the division of her breasts. His mouth lifted a little at the corners. Less than a second had passed, but to Laura it felt like an eternity. Knowing the colour had instantly mounted to her cheeks, she turned quickly away, and very nearly collided with Marie Christine.

She hesitated, suddenly panic-stricken. Marie Christine was imperturbably serving the guests on the wrong side of the table. Surely Zara had said ... Her hands tightened on the bowl she held as she collected herself. It didn't matter. Now there was nothing for it but to cross the room.

Nervously she went to the other side of the table, serving the women first, trying to stand unobtrusively, praying they would both be ignored.

She came to Robert Wentworth last. As she held out the bowl to him she knew her hand was shaking, and she kept her eyes stubbornly lowered. She need not have worried, however. He ignored her totally; she might have been invisible.

Just as she reached the door of the room, he spoke for the first time, his voice cool, clipped, cutting through the conversation around him like a knife.

'Zara,' she heard, 'what *are* those maids of yours wearing? Are they deliberately trying to be provocative?'

Zara gave a nervous laugh.

'They're not maids, Robert darling. It's the children's nanny and the *au pair*. They love to help out. And when they knew you were coming ...' She paused meaningfully, and there was a ripple of laughter.

'Not for my benefit, surely?' His voice sounded cold.

'Well, you know what these girls are like. So silly. And you *are* rather famous, darling ...'

Laura shut the door behind her, seething with anger. How typical of Zara to get the last laugh! she thought furiously. And as for that conceited arrogant prig—well, he'd sounded all too ready to believe her. She marched back to the kitchen, her head held high, and sat grumpily in the corner.

'What did you think of him, then?' Mrs Grove had no need to name names.

'Not much.'

'Incroyable!' Marie Christine raised her eyes dramatically heavenward. *'Un ange un peu diabolique . . .'*

When the bell rang once more and she and Marie Christine returned to the dining room Laura knew her mouth had set sullenly. She served the guests faultlessly, mechanically, not once raising her eyes from the dishes in front of her. This time he looked at her as she approached him, and stood quietly by his side, she was sure of it. She could feel his gaze like scalding water on her skin, but still she kept her eyes obstinately lowered.

A great deal of wine seemed to have been consumed, and Laura had the strong impression that the table was sharing some kind of private joke at her and Marie Christine's expense. She was confirmed in the view when they left the room, and, the moment the door closed, there was a burst of laughter. Oh damn, she thought angrily, seething with frustration. Damn him and damn them. Why had she allowed herself to get caught up in this ridiculous situation?

When they returned at last to serve the final course—Mrs Grove's triumphant soufflé au Grand Marnier—the atmosphere around the table had a curious feeling of suppressed mirth. She saw the women exchange glances, and Zara smiled maliciously. She set her lips, wondering that Marie Christine could be so impervious to it all. Why, for two pins she'd tip the whole soufflé over his beastly arrogant head!

She had reached his side; it was nearly over. Then to her horror, he reached up very deliberately and rested his hand on her bare arm. She flinched, and there was a sudden silence.

'Do let us into the secret.' She saw him glance across at Zara, and then he looked up into her face so she had to meet his eyes. He drawled the words. 'Just why are you two wearing these extraordinary costumes?'

'In spite of what you've been told, not to charm you, Mr Wentworth.' The words came out, perfectly calmly, perfectly audibly, before she could stop them, before she could even think.

Well, that's my job gone, and my diploma with it, she thought, and in that fraction of a second she saw his eyes narrow. Then, totally to her surprise, he laughed, not a fake laugh, but one of genuine amusement.

'Well,' he said, 'so much for your theories, Zara. I thought, somehow, that you might be wrong.'

Then quite calmly, apparently unruffled, he helped himself

to the soufflé. There was nothing Laura could do, and he took his time about it. From where she stood, half behind his chair, she directed a look of hatred at the back of his neck where his hair curled slightly, very dark against the white of his shirt collar.

Then, at the first opportunity, as the general conversation started up once more, she beat a hasty (and, she felt, undignified) retreat.

When she reached the kitchen Marie Christine and Mrs Grove were putting the last coffee cups on Zara's best silver tray. It was one of her old-fashioned affectations to leave the men to port and cigars in the dining room while the women took coffee in the drawing room. Laura glowered at the tray.

'You tired, dear?' Mrs Grove looked at her kindly. 'You look a bit washed out, you know. Why don't you go on up? Marie Christine can do the coffee.'

Silently Laura blessed her. She couldn't face any more of this, she thought suddenly. There was a scene coming, that was inevitable, but she'd face it better, she thought miserably, after a good night's sleep.

'Well, yes, I might. If you don't mind . . .'

Marie Christine did not mind. She was delighted, and quite obviously enjoying herself enormously.

Tiredly, feeling suddenly totally exhausted, Laura went out and climbed the back stairs. It was gone eleven; Jonathan wasn't due for his last feed until midnight; she couldn't go to bed yet anyway. So she sat by the gas-fire in their sitting room. She kicked off her shoes, stretched her legs, reached for a book. But she could not concentrate on it; the words danced in a meaningless jumble before her eyes. She felt curiously restless and on edge, as if she could not settle.

At least she had managed to avoid any more scenes that evening, that was some small comfort. But there would be one in the morning. Would Zara fire her? Dully she tried to weigh up her chances, but even though she knew it was important, she could not concentrate. Her mind circled and jumped; no matter how she tried to discipline or channel it into coherence, it kept coming back to one image, when she had first gone into the room, when the candle had flared . . . What extraordinary eyes he had, she thought. So dark they were almost black, like water at night. Not kind, she thought, and remembered her father.

She stood up, suddenly decisive. This was pointless. She

would give Jonathan his feed now; it was nearly time anyway, and he often woke a little early. Quietly she opened the sitting room door and went out into the little passageway that led past the nurseries. At the far end of the corridor, where the landing led down to the main stairs, one light burned feebly; Zara economised on electricity in this wing of the house. She paused, suddenly tense. The air was heavy with the smell of cigar smoke, and just as she began to move, soft-footed, down the passage, Jonathan's door opened and a tall dark figure came out. She started momentarily.

'Michael?' she said uncertainly.

'Sorry, did I startle you?'

He lurched slightly, shutting the door to the baby's room as she approached him.

'I . . . I was just going to give Jonathan his feed . . .'

'He's still asleep. Don't disturb him yet.'

He stood, blocking her path, swaying slightly on his feet, and Laura's heart sank. He must have put out his cigar, but he was still holding a glass. As she moved, he bent and put it down on the floor, then straightened up uncertainly.

'Whoops!' he chuckled softly. 'Bit unsteady. Good dinner . . .'

His speech was noticeably slurred, and his eyes, as he leaned toward her, reaching for her arm, had that curious unfocused quality they took on when he was seriously drunk.

'Laura . . .'

'Please, Michael.' She tried unsuccessfully to release his hand. 'It's very late. I must give Jonathan his feed . . .'

'Always running off. You're always running off. It's not nice, Laura, not kind. What's the matter, Laura? Don't you like me? I like you, Laura. Sweet little Laura. Such lovely hair . . .'

'Look, Michael, please . . . don't you think you should go back downstairs?'

'Don't want to go downstairs, want to stay here. With lovely Laura. In her lovely dress.' He chuckled, fumbling at the material of the skirt. 'Laura's made my wife cross—very cross. But not me. I think Laura looks . . .' he paused, swaying, trying to focus his eyes on her face.

'Angry?' she asked crisply.

'Not angry. Beautiful. Beautiful hair and beautiful eyes and beautiful breasts . . .' With an accuracy of aim that took her by surprise, he lifted one hand and clamped it with obstinate firmness over the swell of her left breast.

'Right. That's it.' She gave him a firm push. 'You stop this now, Michael, and you go back downstairs!'

He reeled slightly, but she did not dislodge him. Instead he swayed back, bearing her with him, and pressing her against the wall, trapping her with his considerable weight so she could not move. For the first time Laura felt something like panic. He had never gone this far before.

'Please, Michael . . .' she heard her own voice rise nervously in pitch, but Michael took no notice.

'Just one little kiss for Michael . . .'

'No. Stop it!' Laura tried to squirm out of his grasp. His breath, heavy with alcohol, was coming quickly now, and she could tell that—ludicrously drunk though he was—he was becoming aroused. She managed to turn her face away, and the attempted kiss missed her mouth landing somewhere against her hair. This appeared to puzzle him considerably, and seizing her chance, Laura gave him a hefty push. He reeled back, nearly fell, and at the last minute recovered his balance.

'Don't you dare to touch me again!' she hissed at him furiously, keeping her voice low, fearful of waking the girls. 'Not ever, Michael. I've had enough. Now go back downstairs before I call Zara!'

Zara was in fact the last person she would call, but the threat of his wife's ire worked. Michael began to mutter fuddled apologies, and make odd little pleading gestures with his hands, so that Laura felt almost sorry for him. You couldn't dislike Michael, she thought, he was too ridiculous, and too pathetic.

'It doesn't matter now,' she said more gently, and pushed him firmly in the direction of the stairs. 'Just go back and join the others. Go *on*!'

To her relief he did so, weaving his way down the passage to the main stairs. Laura waited anxiously, but obviously he managed to negotiate them somehow, because the expected thump of Michael's falling down them never came. Just as she turned towards Jonathan's door she heard the low laugh. She whirled around, and then froze, staring back down the dimly lit corridor. At the far end, just at the top of the back stairs, leaning nonchalantly against the wall, was Robert Wentworth.

The moon was full, and its light from one of the high dormer windows shone in a square patch against the wall, illuminating the thick black hair, gleaming against the white of his shirt front. He was carrying a bottle, and two glasses, and it was perfectly apparent, from the look of insolent amusement on his face, that he had watched at least part—possibly all—of the scene that had just taken place. As she stared at him, he shifted lazily and, taking his time, came down the passageway towards her.

'Hello,' he said, in tones of infuriating casualness, as if this encounter were totally normal. 'I thought you handled that *awfully* well. My congratulations. I *was* about to come to your aid, then I saw you would cope, so I didn't.'

Laura glared at him. 'I suppose you're drunk as well?' she said, before she could stop herself.

'Drunk?' He considered the question with annoying complacency. 'Not in the least. I get drunk only when I want to, and never when I'm bored. Tonight I was bored.' He paused. 'Most of the time.'

The dark eyes met hers levelly, and Laura felt immediately a curious weakening, a relaxing of her will. She hesitated, knowing he sensed it, and then quickly looked away.

'Yes, well,' she said coldly, 'that's not really my concern. Now if you'll excuse me, I have to give the baby his night feed.'

'So you've been saying—to Michael.' He paused fractionally. 'Do you mind if I watch?'

'Yes, I do,' Laura said hotly. 'You shouldn't be up here at all. I can't think how you . . .'

'Oh, I came up the back way. I've been talking to Mrs Grove, who cooked us such an excellent dinner, and to Marie Christine, the—er—dressmaker . . .' A ghost of a smile came to his lips. 'And now I think I shall talk to you.'

Laura stared at him angrily, unsure what to do. He towered above her, powerful, and clearly immovable. In that moment Jonathan gave a little wail, distinctly aggrieved, and the cry decided her.

'As you like,' she said coldly, opening the door. 'But I have nothing to say to you, and I'd be grateful if you wouldn't disturb the baby.'

'But of course,' he said smoothly, and with a quick movement held back the door for her.

Holding her head high, resolving to ignore him until he gave up this incomprehensible visitation, Laura marched past him, tilting her chin in the air. She switched on a small lamp and went over to the cot. As soon as he saw her, Jonathan gave a gurgle of pleasure and anticipation, and waved his small fists in the air. Instantly Laura's face softened. Making little shushing soothing noises which Jonathan at once understood, she bent over the cot and picked him up. Then, cradling him on her hip with the grace of much practice, she carefully warmed the water, mixed his milk, filled his bottle, tested it for temperature on the inside of her wrist. The familiarity of the procedure soothed her; for a moment she almost forgot the tall silent man who stood in the doorway watching her.

There were two chairs in the room, and when Laura sat down on the low wooden nursing one, next to the lamp, cradling Jonathan against her breasts, Robert Wentworth sat down also, near the door, crossing his legs composedly, his eyes never leaving her face.

'There, there, darling . . .' Laura bent forward, lifting the bottle to the baby's seeking mouth. Two pudgy hands grasped it greedily, and immediately the stillness of the room was punctuated by a steady sucking.

Jonathan was a slow feeder; the minutes lengthened, and as they did so all Laura's tension subsided, and tranquillity took hold of her. The quietness of the room, the gentleness of the light, the little noises of greed and contentment from the baby began to work a strange magic. All sense of the oddness of the situation left her; she accepted it, and the dark watchful man opposite her seemed to accept it also.

When the bottle was finally finished she set it down, and gently lifted Jonathan up against her shoulder. She cradled him there, his small fuzzy head warm against her neck, while she gently stroked his back. After a few minutes of this, Jonathan gave a little preliminary half hiccup and Laura smiled. She patted his bottom, which felt distinctly damp, and Jonathan gave a loud and satisfactory burp. Laura laughed softly, lifting the baby in front of her, and Jonathan waved his arms, as if triumphant. He gurgled, and gave a toothless milky smile. Gently she wiped his face, then rocked him a little in her arms, making the little low crooning noises that were their private language.

'You get on together very well.' Robert Wentworth spoke softly, with a curious sadness in his voice, that made Laura look up at him.

'I've had him since he was born,' she said softly. 'We've had four months to get acquainted.' She stood up. 'I'll have to change him,' she said hesitantly. 'He's soaking wet.' He would leave now, she thought, as she said it. Robert Wentworth was presumably not the kind of man who particularly wanted to be around when it came to nappy changing.

'I'd like to stay.'

'All right,' she said levelly enough, but her heart gave an odd little lurch.

Carefully she brought out the changing mat and laid Jonathan down on it. He liked this part of their ritual, and kicked lustily. While she turned away to find the clean nappy and baby-gro, Robert Wentworth stood up. He approached the tiny figure on the mat cautiously, looking a little uncertain and hesitant for the first time since she had met him, and she repressed a smile.

'Tickle his chest,' she advised gently. 'He likes that. Move slowly, so he has time to get used to you.'

The man bent down, his movements graceful, and with a gentleness that surprised her, knelt, and leaned over the baby. She paused, looking down at him, at the wide powerful shoulders, the thick dark hair. Jonathan had seen him; he gazed unfocusedly up into the dark face bent over him, and made little pouting movements with his mouth. There was a pause; very slowly the man lifted one long narrow tanned hand, and stroked the baby's soft fuzz of hair with one finger. If Jonathan was going to howl he would do it now, she thought, but he didn't. He took his time, then quite suddenly he gurgled. He made little wild grabbing gestures with his hands, most of which missed, but the man let his hand be drawn round; Jonathan finally grasped it, conveyed it straight to his mouth, and sucked at one of his knuckles energetically.

'Such force,' he said softly, 'in such a tiny creature . . . hey!'

Laura laughed.

'Watch out,' she said. 'He isn't teething yet, but he can give you quite a nip.'

She knelt down on the other side of the mat, and gently began to undress Jonathan. Solemnly the man beside her held the nappy and clothes and talcum powder and pins, and handed them to her, each as she needed them. In the circle of the lamplight her movements were deft, yet gentle. When the wet nappy was safely removed, and Jonathan was cleaned and powdered, she let him have a little kick, then carefully pinned him into the clean nappy. When he was finally ready she leaned back on her heels.

'There,' she said. 'One baby, dry and packaged and fed and sleepy and ready for bed.'

'He's quite beautiful.' Robert Wentworth looked down at him, and she saw, looking at him curiously, that the harsh lines of his face had softened. The mouth, which she had judged grim before, curved in a smile of sudden and astonishing warmth. When the dark eyes met hers there was amusement in them.

'The second most beautiful thing I've seen today,' he said seriously, and instantly Laura felt herself tense. She stood up, lifted Jonathan into her arms, and turned away to tuck him into his cot, glad that her face was hidden, that Robert Wentworth should not see how easily he discomposed her.

He had moved to the door, was holding it open for her. He would go now, she thought, and an odd regret tugged at her heart.

'Are your duties finally over, then?' He looked at her quizzically as they stood outside.

She smiled wryly. 'Until the morning, yes.'

He held up two glasses he had brought with him, indicating the bottle under his arm.

'Would you like a drink? I brought it for you.'

'For me?' She stared at him confusedly.

'But of course.'

'But I . . . I don't understand. You shouldn't be up here. It's late . . . they'll be wondering where you are downstairs . . .'

'I couldn't care less. And they won't be. I told them I was leaving, that I was walking home. So?' He looked at her, with a mocking half smile. 'Would you like a drink, yes or no?'

'Well, yes, I would, but . . .'

'No more argument, then. Along here, I think?'

As if it were he who lived here, rather than the other way round, he led the way down the passage, and pushed open the door into the small shabby sitting room. Laura saw his eyebrows lift slightly as he took in its drabness, but he said nothing. Instead, with complete composure he crossed to the windows, drew the curtain, switched on the lamp, and turned up the fire. Then he drew out a chair for her.

'There. Much better.' He looked around the room with an air of satisfaction.

Weakly, half in a daze, not really able to believe this was

happening to her, Laura sat down in the armchair. She stared at him helplessly.

'You could explain,'. she said eventually, as he solemnly poured her some whisky.

'Explain?' He handed her the glass.

'Just a few things. Such as why you're here, how you got here.' She met his gaze levelly, with an apparent confidence and an inner feeling of rising nervousness.

He smiled, and lifted his glass in ironic salute.

'It's quite simple,' he said maddeningly, still totally composed. 'It was becoming, if possible, even more boring downstairs. So, as they say, I made my excuses and left. I said that on account of Michael's excellent port, which in fact I hadn't drunk, but no one noticed that, I preferred not to drive. Once the front door was shut I waited for a while in some rather damp rhododendrons—not pleasant, that. Then I came in the back door, and had a little chat to Mrs Grove and your friend Marie Christine in the kitchen. They assured me that you would be delighted to see me, that they could think of nothing nicer than to continue to sit and gossip round the kitchen table, so that we should be totally undisturbed. And Mrs Grove very generously provided me with the whisky from Michael's cellar. So here I am.' He looked around him. 'Up in the nursery wing, with the children's nurse.' His eyes met hers. 'Or possibly with an extremely provocative French maid—I'm really not sure which.'

In spite of her nervousness, Laura laughed, responding to the wicked gleam of amusement in his dark eyes.

'You know about all that, then?' she said. 'Marie Christine told you?'

'Oh yes,' he said, 'I know all about that. And quite a lot about you, Laura.' He paused, speaking her name with a curious emphasis that brought the colour to her cheeks. 'Laura Kent.'

She started, spilling a little of her drink nervously.

'Oh yes, I know your name. And your age. Twenty-two, I think?' He crossed to her and stood looking down at her, his face suddenly serious. 'And just a few other things. Including, unless I'm mistaken, the fact that you're going to find yourself unemployed in the morning.'

There was a sudden silence. Laura just sat looking up at him, unable to speak. Then, stiffly, feeling hurt constrict her throat, she bent forward and put down her drink.

'I see,' she said softly, and the tears started up behind her eyes. She had known it, of course, from the moment in the dining-room, when she had been so rude. But having it confirmed, so suddenly, by a stranger, by this dark perturbing man, made it somehow more shocking and more painful. She heard herself give an odd, choked little sob, and the tears spilled over, hot against her flushed cheeks.

'Here . . .' Before she could move, he knelt down beside her and drew her to him with great gentleness. But his kindness, the solemnly proffered amd immaculately laundered white handkerchief, made it worse. Out of strain and tiredness, and perhaps, she thought in confusion, as she clung to him, out of grief so long repressed, she cried, brokenly, as she had never cried before. Her tears spilled over on to his dinner jacket, but he seemed not to mind. He simply held her firmly in his arms, circling her with their warmth, holding her head against his powerful shoulder, and just occasionally stroking her hair, until, after a little while, she calmed and the tears gradually ceased.

'I'm sorry,' he said, at last, very gently. 'I shouldn't have told you like that. It was crass and stupid. I thought . . .'

'No, please.' She raised her tear-stained face to him. 'It doesn't matter. I'd rather hear it from you, now, than from . . .' She broke off.

'From Zara?' He spoke the name contemptuously, with a coldness that frightened her. She nodded silently.

There was a brief silence, and gradually Laura regained control of her breathing. Shakily she handed back the damp handkerchief, and gave him a rueful smile.

'I'm sorry,' she said. 'I've ruined your handkerchief, and I'm being ridiculous. I never cry. It's just that . . . that I've become very fond of the children, you see. One shouldn't, I know. They told us that at college. That one had to learn to . . . to be unemotional about it.' Her voice broke a little, then recovered strength. 'You have to be detached, you see, all the time. Because you always have to move on—leave them behind. They're their parents' children, after all.' She smiled, a little wanly. 'I expect I'll learn, eventually.'

His face hardened. 'I shouldn't learn too fast if I were you. It sounds most unnatural to me . . .' He broke off, his eyes darkening, and then stood up with an angry impatient gesture. 'Why the hell can't women look after their own children?'

Laura smiled at the arrogance of his manner. 'That's not always possible, you know,' she said reasonably. 'Suppose they work—suppose they want to work. Or have to travel a lot. Someone has to look after the children.'

'Zara doesn't work,' he turned on her angrily, and she was surprised at the vehemence of his tone.

'Well, no,' she said hesitantly, 'as it happens, she doesn't. But more and more women do, and so—if they can afford someone good, reliable, someone they can trust their children with—why not?' She smiled. 'The whole thing is a growth industry. Ask at my college. They can't train enough people to meet the demand.'

'Is that why you took this on—because you think it's a growth industry?' He looked at her scornfully.

'No, of course not,' she said quickly. 'I took it on because I wanted to. I like children.'

'So marry and have some of your own,' he said, with a trace of sympathy in his voice.

'That situation didn't arise,' she said hotly, stung by his tone.

'Didn't it?' The dark eyes met hers. 'You surprise me. Where have you been hiding yourself these last few years then, Laura Kent? In a nunnery?'

'Certainly not!' She stood up, feeling her cheeks flush with anger at the sarcasm in his voice. She forced herself to meet his eyes, and keep her voice level. 'As it happens, I wanted to work. I wanted a career. Oh, I'm sure it doesn't sound much of one to someone like you, of course, but . . .'

'You're right, it doesn't,' he snapped. 'Being passed around from pillar to post, treated like a servant by people like Zara who are stuffed full of social pretensions and can't be bothered to look after their own children. Being exploited, stuck up here in a dingy attic, taking your meals in the kitchen. God, it's unbelievable—it's nineteenth century! And for what? So you can be dumped the minute the children are old enough to go to school? Did you think it was going to be like that? Or did you have some cosier picture? Perhaps you thought it was going to be like *Brideshead Revisited* or something, that you'd age gracefully into a valued family retainer, with your own little room upstairs, and all the great-grandchildren coming to bring you flowers and kisses?'

'No, of course I didn't think that!' She glared at him angrily. 'And in any case, it's none of your business. I can't think why we're having this conversation. I wouldn't expect a

film actor to understand anyway . . .' She broke off, aware she
had gone too far, appalled at her own rudeness. They were
standing very close to one another, and suddenly Laura felt
herself intensely aware of their proximity, as if the brief space
of air that separated them reverberated with an electrical
charge. To her surprise he took the insult; his lips lifted in a
slow, dangerous smile.

'You're quite right,' he said. 'I can't think why we're having
this conversation. In fact, I can't think why we're having any
conversation at all.'

He stepped forward, and very slowly, deliberately, lifted his
hand to her face, brushing back the thick curtain of hair that
fell forwards over her shoulders. Laura stared at him, unable
to move. Very delicately, very gently he moved his hand
across her cheek, tracing the outline of her face, her mouth.
For one insane moment she thought he was about to kiss her,
and at once knew her eyes widened nervously; but he did not.
He let his hand fall and stepped back to a more decorous
distance. There was a glint of amusement in his eyes, as if he
knew what she thought, and Laura blushed crimson.

'Is a film actor, as you so contemptuously put it, permitted
to ask what you intend to do if you have to leave here?' he
said finally.

Laura shrugged. 'I don't know,' she said stiffly. 'Obviously
I haven't had much time to think . . .' She looked away
carefully. 'I'm sure I could find another job.'

'I'm sure you could.' He paused. 'Zara mentioned
something though. Some problem. Something about a
diploma . . .'

'You mean she discussed it? All that? With her guests?'

'Not with all the guests. With me. She thought I might
understand about what she called the "servant problem".'

Laura sighed. Why should he care? she thought tiredly. The
kind of problems she faced couldn't be more remote from him
and his world; as far as she was concerned, he was a creature
from a different planet. But obviously he was waiting for
some kind of explanation, so she began again, keeping her
voice deliberately cool and impersonal.

'It's quite simple,' she said. 'I did two years' training in
college. After that, to qualify, you have to do a probationary
year, with a family. If their report is good, you pass—you're a
registered nursery nurse. If it's not . . .' She left the sentence
unfinished, seeing his face darken, as if with anger.

'I see.' There was a pause, then he looked at his watch, and Laura suddenly felt her heart sink. Why had she said anything? Obviously she was boring him, and after all, what concern was it of his? Tomorrow he'd probably be leaving the village; he might be going anywhere in the world. To him, all this could hardly be more trivial.

'I'm sorry,' she said stiffly, 'But if you don't mind, I'm terribly tired now, and there's no reason why I should inflict all this on you, so . . .'

'I should go?' He smiled. 'I'm sure you're right.'

Laura felt her heart give a little lurch of disappointment, and cursed herself inwardly.

At the door he paused.

'Tell me,' he said, in a flippant tone of voice, 'do you wear a uniform . . . as a nursery nurse?'

She looked at him in surprise, and then, in spite of herself, smiled.

'Oh yes,' she said. 'Zara ordered it from Harrods. You'd like it very much—brown lisle stockings, brown overalls, white apron. And for outdoors a rather thick brown tweed coat, and a horrible little hat with a badge on the front. Gloves on when pushing the pram, of course.'

He laughed. 'Yes, I get the picture. Well, don't wear it tomorrow, will you?'

'Tomorrow?' she stared at him blankly.

'When I take you out to lunch.'

'What?'

'Lunch. Luncheon. Food. You know, in the middle of the day.' He smiled at her mockingly. 'I'll be here at one to pick you up. The front door, not the tradesmen's entrance. And do try to be punctual—I detest women who are late.'

'But . . .'

'No buts. You're coming. I need your advice, you see.' He gave her a dazzling smile, designed to make any woman's knees grow weak, she thought, as hers did. 'After all, you'll be more or less a free agent, won't you? And if Zara makes any trouble, tell her to go to hell. I would.'

With which parting shot, he inclined his head briefly in a gesture of farewell, disappeared through the door, and closed it behind him. Laura stared after him in stupefaction. Then she laughed. He knew how to make an effective exit, she thought—not that that was surprising. And she could just imagine him telling Zara to go to hell—or anyone, for that

matter. She paused as, gradually, a feeling of enormous
elation took possession of her. A free agent! Her heart lifted.
Suddenly she felt a ridiculous impulse to do something
absurd: to dance, to sing, to shout.

She flopped into a chair, laughing at her own idiocy. She
stretched her legs and stared unseeingly at the ceiling,
wondering exactly how this extraordinary man, in the space of
less than an hour, had given her back something she'd begun
to feel she had lost for ever. *I feel free*, she thought; and
instead of looming, dull, before her, the future beckoned,
bright, dangerous perhaps, but rich with possibility.

When she finally went to bed, the memory of his features,
of that harshly planed face and odd perturbing eyes, was so
sharply etched in her memory that she thought, as she closed
her eyes, that she must inevitably dream of him. And that
wasn't such an unpleasant prospect, she thought wryly, as she
composed herself for sleep. But she did not. Instead she
dreamed she was in a great silver car, speeding very fast down
an endless sunlit road.

She was alone in the car; she was driving.

CHAPTER THREE

'WHAT did she say, then?' Mrs Grove, furious at missing the
scene because she had been sent to shop in the village, was all
curiosity. 'She can't just have told you to go—not just like
that!'

Laura laughed. 'More or less. Not her language, but
certainly her sentiments.'

Mrs Grove pursed her lips. 'And what about that Marie
Christine? It were all her idea. Did you tell her that?'

Laura shook her head. 'No, of course not.' She smiled.
'Marie Christine was let off with a warning. I, however, was in
a position of greater responsibility, so my sin was the worse.'

'Eh, I don't know.' Mrs Grove clicked her tongue
sympathetically, and placed a large mug full of steaming tea
in front of Laura. 'It's not right, you know. It weren't your
fault—and it were only a prank. No harm done. And after all
you done for those kids of hers . . .'

Laura sighed. This morning she had woken filled with

energy, the elation of the previous night still with her. It had
carried her through the brief scene with Zara, had lasted
really until now. But now, as one o'clock approached, it was
beginning to desert her. When Zara had so coldly, so crisply,
informed her that she could more or less pack her bags and
depart as soon as possible, and that no reference would be
forthcoming, she had said it with such obvious relish that
Laura had almost pitied her. How awful, how ugly, she had
thought, to be bound by such petty malice. But now the
reality of her situation was beginning to come home to her.
She had a little money saved; apart from that she had
nothing. Nowhere to go, no job.

'I'll miss the children,' she said hesitantly, as Mrs Grove
levered her weight into the chair beside her.

''Course you will—you was like a mother to them. How
they going to take it? You told them yet?'

Laura shook her head, 'No. Sammy and Jessy are spending
the day over at the Ryders', it was fixed weeks ago. Anyway,
Zara's going to tell them. She insisted on that.'

'Get her oar in first, you mean?' Mrs Grove shook her
head. '*I* see.'

'I'm sure it'll be all right,' said Laura, sounding more
confident than she felt. 'They seem attached to people at that
age, but really they adapt very quickly. A month from now,
they won't remember my name.' And at the thought of
leaving them all, of never seeing the children again, a lump
came to her throat. Mrs Grove looked at her keenly.

'So,' she said, 'that's them. What about you? What are you
going to do, my dear, that's what I want to know?'

Laura looked at her, and then, anxious to deflect her,
laughed.

'I haven't the least idea, in the long term,' she said. 'But in
the short term—well, this is technically my day off. And in ten
minutes I'm being taken out to lunch. By Mr Wentworth.'

Mrs Grove's eyebrows rose so high they disappeared
underneath the little tightly permed curls that fell over her
forehead.

'*I* see,' she said finally. 'That's the lie of the land, is it? Well,
after last night I can't say as it's altogether a surprise.' She
paused, and then gave a robust chuckle. 'Nearly jumped out
of my skin, I did, when I heard him a-tapping at the back
door last night. Didn't know it was him then, of course. So I
opens up, and in he marches, as cool as a cucumber. Wicked

sense of humour he's got, and sharp as a knife. Saw through *her* pretty quick, I'll warrant . . .' She broke off. 'So, when he says he wants to have a word with you, and I says you'll be up feeding the baby—well, I didn't ought to have let him go up, I suppose. But he's got a way with him, he has.' She paused suddenly, her eyes becoming serious. 'So he's after taking you out now, is that it? Does *she* know? That ought to settle her jib good and proper, that should.'

Laura laughed. 'She doesn't know,' she said quickly. 'And for your information, he's not "taking me out". He wants my advice, that's all.'

Mrs Grove nodded, her face expressionless. 'Go on then, dear. Want to look your best, don't you?'

Yes, she supposed she did, Laura thought, as she hurried up the stairs to her room. Not that there was much point in that. Robert Wentworth habitually escorted some of the world's loveliest women, so he was hardly likely to be impressed by her efforts. And anyway, this was obviously supposed to be a formal meeting, at which she gave him whatever advice it was he wanted—though she couldn't imagine how she, of all people, could be of any assistance to him. But still . . . In her room she looked in the long glass. She had changed out of her uniform and put on her best dress. It was three years old now; her father had bought it for her. It couldn't be said to be fashionable, but it was pretty. It was made of wool, and was a soft wine colour, its neckline edged with lace. She ran a brush through her long thick hair, wondered whether she should tie it back, and then, nervously realising she might be late if she experimented, she hastened down into the hall, praying silently that Zara—as she had said she would be—was resting.

As she reached the bottom of the stairs she heard a car door slam, and she just managed to open the front door before he knocked. His hand was already raised to the door, and her speed almost propelled her into his arms. Quickly he lowered his hand to steady her, and laughed.

'Such eagerness!' he said. 'I'm very flattered.' He drew back. 'And such exemplary . . .' his eyes travelled over her face as if admiringly, 'punctuality,' he finished, in a tone that implied he didn't refer to that at all.

Laura looked at him a little crossly. 'I . . . I just didn't want you to disturb Zara,' she said reluctantly.

'I see. This is to be a clandestine assignation, is it? Then if you're quite ready, perhaps I'd better whisk you straight off in my car. Is there anything you need by way of disguise? Headscarf perhaps, dark glasses . . .?'

'Don't be ridiculous.' Laura stepped out on to the porch and banged the front door unnecessarily loudly. 'As you said last night, I'm a free agent.'

She saw him give her a brief searching look, but he said nothing, merely taking her arm lightly and leading her down the steps to the car. He opened the door for her and helped her in, then came round and lowered himself into the seat beside her.

Laura glanced at him covertly as he reached for the ignition; he was looking, she thought weakly, totally devastating. His shirt, of cream silk, was open to the throat; his long powerful legs and narrow hips were encased in tight, somewhat worn cord trousers. Over the shirt was a loose jacket of dark brown suede. He looked incredible—and also as if he had made no effort whatsoever to do so.

The powerful engine roared into life and she looked quickly out of the window, attempting an air of complete nonchalance—as if, she thought to herself with wry amusement, film stars like this one drove up every day of the week and helped her into the deep leather seats of silver-grey Mercedes.

'O.K.?' He paused, holding the car back, his hand on the gear lever.

'Fine,' she said, turning back. 'Oh!' She stared.

'What's the matter?'

'Nothing. Just the sunglasses . . .' He had put on black glasses that were impenetrable, and she realised instantly how much safer she felt when she could read the expression in his eyes.

'Yes, well, I'm sorry about that. I'll take them off now, if you like.' He did so, and smiled, letting in the gear. 'But I'll put them on later, if you don't mind. They have their uses, you see.'

'Why?' She stared at him curiously as the car sped down the Fielding's drive.

He gave her a sideways glance. 'Well, occasionally I get recognised when I go out in public. And I don't like it.'

'Nonsense,' she said robustly, before she could stop herself. 'In Warwickshire, in March? I can't think of anything more calculated to make everyone stare at you!'

'And you think that's what I really want?' His mouth tightened. 'Why not say what you mean?'

Laura hesitated. 'Well,' she said placatingly, 'you must be used to it by now. I'd have thought . . .'

'You'd be wrong.' He pulled the car up abruptly at the end of the drive and then accelerated out on to the road with a screech of tyres. 'I detest it. I always have and I always shall. And you never get used to it.'

She stared at him curiously, surprised by the vehemence in his tone.

'But surely,' she said more gently, 'it's part of what you are, isn't it? You're a . . . well, a public figure.'

'That doesn't make me public property.' He kept his eyes on the road ahead, never looking at her, accelerating up through the gears very fast. There was a brief heavy silence, and Laura felt her heart sink.

'We might as well get one thing clear from the start.' He spoke suddenly, startling her, his voice icy cold. 'I'm an actor. As it happens I work in films. It's a job, like any other. You clearly don't think much of it, and you're entitled to your opinion. But it would help a good deal if you'd put aside all those preconceived opinions and prejudices. In fact . . .' he slammed his palm against the steering wheel, 'it would help a good deal if you could damn well forget I was an actor.'

'Forget you're famous?' She gave him a sideways glance under her lashes.

'Above all that. Yes, goddamit!'

'Treat you like a perfectly ordinary man?'

He caught the mockery in her voice, and glanced at her suspiciously.

'It's what I am.' He turned away, his mouth set in a hard line.

'All right.' She smiled. 'Then you're driving too fast. And you generally do. Three months ago you nearly knocked me into a ditch.'

'*What?*' He slowed, then laughed. 'Did I really?'

'Yes, you did.' Their eyes met for a brief second, then he turned his attention back to the road, driving noticeably less dangerously.

'Well, that puts me in my place, doesn't it?' he said eventually. 'And what did you think, Miss Nursery Nurse, when this arrogant actor nearly knocked you down?'

She smiled. 'I thought he was an arrogant actor, of course. In a very ostentatious car.'

'And what do you think now?' He glanced at her flirtatiously.

'Now?' She stretched luxuriously. 'Oh, now I think it's the most wonderful, comfortable car in the world.'

'And the actor?'

'He improves upon acquaintance.'

'Is that all?' He managed to sound convincingly disappointed, and Laura smiled to herself. As if he cared, she thought.

'I'm reserving judgment.'

'Don't reserve it too long,' he said grimly. 'Or I might take things into my own hands, and start pressurizing your judgment.'

That seemed to Laura a distinctly enticing possibility. It occurred to her, as they drove through the narrow winding lanes, as the sun suddenly burst forth from behind the clouds, vitalising the whole landscape, that she felt wildly, absurdly quite lightheadedly happy, and that the main cause of it was the man sitting beside her. It also occurred to her that it would be much safer and much more sensible to curb all such feelings, since they would inevitably lead to disappointment and heartache. However, she thought, just at this moment, just for this one time—I don't care. She laughed softly, and he immediately glanced across at her.

'You be careful,' he said, with mock sternness. 'You've had fair warning.' As he spoke he reached his hand across, and very lightly touched hers, where it lay in her lap. He removed it instantly; her happiness, to her dismay, redoubled.

He was taking the road, she saw, that skirted the town of Stratford-upon-Avon; soon they crossed the county border into Gloucestershire; the road began to wind, and in the distance the Cotswold hills curved green and mellow brown. Red brick and half-timbering gave way to houses of soft grey Cotswold stone, their dipped roofs patterned with lichen. The sun was brilliant; under the hedges, as they passed, Laura glimpsed patches of primroses.

'It's spring,' she said happily. 'The first day of spring. Isn't it beautiful?'

'It certainly feels that way.' He gave her a sideways glance. 'It's not as idyllic as it looks, though, you know. This is witch country.'

'Witch country?' she looked at him in surprise. 'You can't mean it!'

'I certainly can. You see that hill?' He indicated a tall rounded hill to their left, its crown lopsidedly circled with a thick clump of pines and oak. 'That's Meon Hill. Celebrated for witchcraft since the sixteenth century. There are still cabalistic signs on the trees up there. And on All Hallows Eve ...' He sank his voice to a chilling whisper, and Laura laughed, a little uneasily. For some reason she was reminded, for an instant, of Sammy's tale of the ghost of Marston Court. His house. She cleared her throat.

'You don't believe in all that, surely?'

'Certainly I do.' He smiled. 'I'm an actor, and all actors have a very healthy regard for ... superstitions.'

He spoke lightly, but there was an edge of seriousness in his tone, and Laura looked at him curiously.

'Your house,' she said hesitantly. 'Marston. That's supposed to be haunted, isn't it? Sammy told me.'

'Haunted?' He didn't look at her, kept his eyes on the road. 'There's some such story, I believe. But then it's an old house, it would be surprising if there weren't.' His tone was dismissive, and Laura judged it better not to pursue the subject. In any case, she was diverted. They were coming into the village of Broadway, one of the loveliest in the Cotswolds, and he slowed as they turned down the wide central street. With pleasure Laura looked around her; she had wanted to come here before, on one of her days off. But as those days had gradually been encroached upon by Zara's demands, she had never made it. Now the houses looked almost gold in the warm light; boxes of crimson and russet wallflowers brightened their windows; in the summer, she knew, the place would be filled with tourists and motor coaches; now it was almost deserted, extraordinarily peaceful and calm.

'The restaurant's just down here, on the Snowshill road.' He pulled off the road suddenly, turned into a drive through a high yew hedge, and pulled up the car with a crunch of gravel in front of a tall rambling house, its Georgian façade softened by vines and winter jasmine. 'Have you been here before? It has quite a reputation now.'

Laura laughed. 'Here? Of course not. Nursery nurses don't get taken to places like this.'

'They do today. Come on.'

Taking her arm, he led her in through the wide portico and into a beautiful hallway. Its floor was black and white marble; the air was rich with the scent of wood smoke from the huge fire that burned in the grate. It wasn't like a restaurant at all, Laura thought, looking around her curiously. There was a small discreet reception desk; apart from that it might have been a private country house.

'Robert?' They turned as a young man came towards them; for a second Laura hesitated, then she remembered him. Of course—Hugh Clancy, Zara's friend. This must be the restaurant she had heard so much about. 'Good morning. I've kept your usual table . . .' He broke off, staring at Laura for a second longer than was strictly polite, then she saw his eyes widen. He recollected himself quickly. 'Laura,' he said warmly. 'How nice.' He turned to Robert Wentworth with an easy smile. 'Laura and I met at tea once—at Zara's.' He paused fractionally, a hint of amusement in his warm brown eyes. 'And last night, after a fashion, of course.'

'The less said about that the better,' said Laura lightly, and Hugh laughed.

'Oh, I don't know,' he said, and she saw his eyes travel quickly and lightly over her, taking in what she was wearing. 'But I must say it's a revelation, seeing you out of uniform. Don't you think, Robert?'

'I think we should go in.' To her surprise his tone was less than gracious; his expression scowling. Hugh instantly adopted a soothing tone.

'But of course. Through here.' He led them into a long room, with tall windows looking out over the gardens. 'Can I bring you something to drink?'

Robert Wentworth looked at Laura enquiringly.

'Er—sherry,' she said, suddenly nervous, and to her relief saw his face lighten. He repressed a smile.

'What a good idea. Dry? Two dry sherries, Hugh. Chilled, I think.'

Hugh nodded, set the menus on the table, and taking the hint, left them quickly.

Robert Wentworth leaned back in his chair, surveying the room. There were only a few other couples, and if they had recognised him, they were ignoring him with a studious English discretion. He had put on the dark glasses when they got out of the car; now he removed them. As his eyes met hers, ironic, darkly speculative, Laura felt again the strange weakening sensation she had whenever he looked at her. She picked up the menu and began to study it intently, the French terms swimming on the page before her.

'Would you let me order for you?'

'Oh, yes, please.' Gratefully she put the menu down, then immediately wished she hadn't. Now she couldn't escape that dry watchful regard. Suddenly she felt unbelievably tongue-tied and gauche, and she cursed herself, her mind spinning. If only she could think of something light and sophisticated to say, something that would indicate she wasn't in the least overawed. Scraps of phrases, inane remarks, battled in her mind. She opened her mouth to say something, then shut it again. She was grateful when the wine waiter brought their drinks, and when another waiter arrived to take their order. Robert Wentworth discussed the menu with him, then took his time selecting the wine. As he did so, glad his attention was diverted, she looked at him carefully.

It was odd, she thought, to sit opposite someone you hardly knew, yet whose face was as familiar to you as an old friend's. He looked now exactly as he did on screen; except that the force of his presence was even more powerful, more magnetic. Impossible to say where it came from, that force. His voice was low; his gestures, as he made their order, contained, minimal. There was nothing extrovert or loud about him, no effort to dominate or impress. Rather there was a curious negligence, a hint of hauteur, in the easy grace with which he sat, in the tilt of his jaw. The beauty of his face; the harsh masculine perfection of its lines—that was disturbing, of course, it held the gaze irresistibly. But it was not that which made the face so compelling; it was something in the mouth, she thought; in its sensuality. And above all something in the eyes. His habitual expression, she realised, was mocking, detached, as if he never ceased to survey the world around him and found it slightly ridiculous. But just occasionally that guarded look shifted. And when it did there was something in his eyes that frightened her, a danger and a pain. From nowhere she remembered the days of her father's illness; of reading aloud to him: *Paradise Lost*, and Milton's first description of Satan. *For now the thought, Both of lost happiness and lasting pain, Torments him . . .*

She blushed as he turned back to her, catching her gaze. She was being absurd, she thought quickly. Why on earth had her mind made that association? *Lost happiness*—what application did that have to this man? He had anything anyone could want; and more.

'Now.' He cut across her thoughts, startling her, and raised his glass, his eyes glinting with amusement. 'To the continued improvement of our . . . acquaintance.'

Laura smiled, and sipped the pale gold sherry. Deliciously cool, it instantly warmed the throat and the stomach, returning her a little of her courage.

'I thought . . .' he paused, his eyes intent on her face. 'I thought—just to begin with, you understand—that you might tell me a little about yourself. Just a few things. Your life story.'

Laura laughed. 'My life story? It wouldn't take long to tell.'

'Then tell away.' He leaned back in his chair, unconsciously adopting the position in which he had been sitting when she saw him first the previous night, his arm lolling against the back of his chair, his body relaxed; his eyes dangerously alert. I shan't be intimidated, Laura thought.

'Very well.' She met his gaze evenly. 'I was born in Cairo; my father worked for the British Council—arranging visiting art exhibitions from England, theatre company tours— cultural propaganda, if you like.' She smiled. 'So we never lived in any one place very long. We went where he was posted. Egypt, France—Bulgaria for a while. My mother died when I was ten, and after that I went to boarding school in England, because my father couldn't cope with me abroad. We were taught by nuns, and I learned nothing at all . . .' She hesitated. 'Then, when I was seventeen, my father became quite ill; he'd contracted T.B. out in India, on one of his postings. So . . .' she paused, 'I lived with him in London. I nursed him a bit. The T.B. was in control—it just left him very tired, and excitable. He hated it. He loved to be out and doing things, meeting friends, going to the theatre, talking late into the night. All of which was bad for him. So . . .' she shrugged. 'We were short of money; his pension wasn't large. I decided to train—I thought, you see, that I might be able to get a job as a nanny in London, so I'd still be able to see him . . . look after him a bit.' She hesitated, and looked away. 'Then he was killed, just over a year ago now. He . . . he was knocked down, in Piccadilly. It must have been very quick, painless, they said. So . . .' She sighed. 'Well, you know the rest. There was nothing to keep me in London any more, so I took the job with Zara and Michael. I've been with them almost a year.'

'I'm sorry.' Her hand was resting on the white tablecloth, and he covered it gently, for a moment, with his own. The words, the gesture, were conventional enough, but Laura instantly felt the sense of comfort, or refuge, he had given her the night before.

'No brothers or sisters?'

She shook her head. 'No.'

'I haven't either,' he said, and she saw his face darken. 'Not now.' He seemed about to say more, but at that moment the waiter arrived with their food, and the fussing with the plates, the subdued yet theatrical presentation of the dishes, distracted them both.

'What is it? It looks delicious.' Laura stared at the tiny fluted dishes before them.

'It's a fish soufflé. And this ...' he indicated the silver sauce-boat, 'is lobster sauce. It's usually very good. I've had it here before.'

How often had he been here, then? Laura caught herself thinking. And with whom? But she pushed the thought away crossly; what business was it of hers? Carefully she tasted a little of the soufflé, a little of the delicate sauce. She sighed contentedly.

'It's *amazing*! I've never tasted anything so delicious.'

He smiled. 'Hugh doesn't do things by halves. He has a new chef—French, trained at the Tour d'Argent. He wants to be the first English country restaurant to win three stars in Michelin.'

Laura ate with gusto. 'I should think he will be,' he said. 'Not that I'm qualified to judge, but this is wonderful.'

He watched her eat with amusement, eating only a little himself. When she had finished she put down her fork with a sigh.

'I suppose you eat in restaurants like this all the time?' She smiled. 'It's a great treat for me.'

He eyed her solemnly. 'Oh, all the time.'

Laura blushed defensively at the mockery in his eyes.

'Well,' she said, 'you must lead a very exotic life. Travelling all over the world ... visiting wonderful places.' She paused. 'Are you staying at Marston long, this time?'

'Unfortunately, no. A couple more days at most.' He looked away, and Laura felt her heart give an obstinate lurch of disappointment. He looked back, meeting her eyes. 'I'm filming at the moment, in New Mexico. I just have a short break out.' He paused. 'There was some business I had to attend to at Marston.'

'I see.' She looked down, hoping fervently that the disappointment she felt wasn't betrayed on her face. 'Is it ... an interesting film?'

He laughed shortly. 'Not very. Good director—Sam Kitzbuhl. I worked with him on *Thunder at Morning*.'

'Oh, I saw that.'

'Did you? Did you like it?'

'Very much.'

'Well, this is a little similar. But the screenplay's not so good. Thwarted passion—an affair of the heart.' He grinned. 'It all comes out very badly in the end.'

'It sounds terrific.'

He laughed. 'You, young lady, have obviously an unhealthy taste for melodrama! Now ...' he leaned back as the waiters prepared to serve the next course, 'see if you like this as much as the soufflé.'

The next course was venison, though Laura wouldn't have known that had he not told her. It was sliced very thin, served with a sauce of wine and chestnuts, and with tiny potatoes gently sautéed in butter. They ate companionably, while he told her more about the film, about working in New Mexico. When she had finished she leaned back, smiling seraphically.

'That was *wonderful*,' she said. 'It was the most delicious meal I've ever had.'

'You won't have pudding?' He smiled at her. 'There's masses of them, each more calorific than the last.'

'I'd love to, but I couldn't.' She grinned at him. 'I couldn't eat another thing.'

'You disappoint me.' He leaned forward. 'You have no idea how refreshing it is to take someone out to a meal who actually enjoys it. Most women now ... well, they have a little grilled fish, a few lettuce leaves, endless glasses of iced Perrier. Very depressing—more like a wake than a celebration.'

Laura laughed. 'They're probably wise. They'll all stay as slender as can be. Whereas I ...' She broke off, suddenly depressed by a vision in which Robert Wentworth had an endless succession of meals with tall, impossibly thin, impossibly beautiful women.

'Whereas you ...' he leaned forward, 'are very young, and very natural and very much more fun. And as I imagine you know perfectly well, need have no worries whatsoever on that score. So don't fish for compliments.' His eyes travelled lazily,

languidly, from her face to her high young breasts, then back
to her face. Laura blushed crimson.

'I was doing no such thing!' she said hotly.

'Really?' He looked at her mockingly. 'Then I'll pay you
one. You look extremely beautiful—especially when you
blush. And you may not have noticed, but the waiter has been
casting languorous looks in your direction from the moment
we walked in. And so . . .' he pushed back his chair, 'unless
you feel you must have coffee now, we'll go, I think. Would
you mind?'

'Oh no, of course not.' Hurriedly Laura began to gather up
her bag. She was boring him, she thought; all through the
meal, he'd been bored. She had been enjoying herself so much
she'd almost forgotten how naïve and dull she must seem to
him. He came round, moving a little faster than the waiter he
had referred to, and pulled back her chair for her. Laura
couldn't meet his eyes. She knew she was scarlet with
embarrassment. While he was settling the bill, and talking to
Hugh, she ducked quickly into the ladies' room, thankful that
it was both cool and empty. She looked at her face in the
glass, and addressed herself firmly. Right, she thought, stop
being a fool. Stop behaving like a star-struck teenager. Calm
down and make sensible conversation on the drive back.

She splashed her face with cold water, brushed her hair,
and after a few minutes felt calmer. All she had to do was
remain calm for the half hour it took to get back to the
Fieldings' house. Then say goodbye, and wish him a good
flight back to America. Her heart felt dull and leaden, but she
managed to look poised and confident—or hoped she did—
when she walked out to find him waiting for her, watching her
cross the hallway to him.

'You didn't mention . . .' she said tentatively in the car as he
got in beside her. 'Perhaps you've changed your mind, but
you did say you wanted my advice . . .' Her voice tailed away,
as he looked at her quizzically.

'So I do.'

'Oh, well, perhaps as we drive back . . .'

He gave her a brilliant smile. 'No hurry,' he said. 'We have
all afternoon. I'm taking you back to Marston.'

CHAPTER FOUR

'I WANT you to see the house first, then I'll explain.'

He took her hand as he helped her from the car, and at the touch, quick, firm, against her skin, Laura felt a current of extraordinary attraction shoot through her body. In the same moment, avoiding his eyes, she saw the house properly for the first time, from close to. And so, even afterwards, she could never be sure of her reactions to it—whether they had been to the house, or to the man, or perhaps both. Whichever it was, it stopped her dead in her tracks; she stood quite still staring before her, aware that his eyes never left her face, yet powerless to turn to him.

They had driven up in sunlight, but the afternoon was changeable, with clouds now scudding across what had been a clear sky. As she got out of the car the sun dimmed, and so she saw the house for the first time in a sombre light. It was undeniably beautiful; Jacobean, built of grey Cotswold stone, the steeply pitched roof decorated with fantastical pinnacles, its leaded light windows, unexpectedly large, looking clear out across the valley. Over the entrance was a clock, with a blue face, bearing the inscription *Tempus fugit*. Time did not flee here, however; the clock had stopped at two. Against the walls roses were trained; even so early in the year she could recognise them, for her father had loved gardens. Gloire de Dijon, Honorine de Brabant, Albertine. One of the roses had broken free from the tracery of wires that held it in place; in the breeze it moved, scratching against the walls with a dry restless sound. The windows, impenetrably dark, looked like so many eyes. Laura shivered.

'Come inside.' He took her arm. 'I think I know what you feel. It affects me like that too—always.'

To her surprise he opened the front door himself, then led her into an enormous hall. It was floored with slate, which gave a chill to the air, even though the central heating was on. But then the radiators, obviously old-fashioned, could hardly cope with heating such a huge space. Robert smiled at her encouragingly

'I'm more or less camping here,' he said wryly. 'My

housekeeper comes in normally from the Lodge—but she's been ill, so I told her not to bother much as I'm only here for a few days. Come on—we'll go into the morning room. It's less oppressive, and I can light a fire there.'

He opened one of several doors that led off the hall, and took her into a room that looked out over the gardens.

'Oh,' she said involuntarily, 'it's beautiful!'

The room was of a much less daunting size, although, Laura thought with a smile, you could still have fitted into it all the tiny rooms from the London flat she had shared with her father. But it was square, its panelling painted white, and it was very pretty. A woman's room, she thought instinctively, looking around at the deep sofas, covered with exquisite flower-patterned chintzes, at the small round tables, the Chinese lamps, the Worcester porcelain carefully arranged on the white marble chimneypiece.

Robert Wentworth bent over the fire, piling logs on it, getting the flames to catch. While he did so she wandered around the room, looking idly at the beautiful things it contained; the tall Chinese lacquered secretaire; the collection of carved ivory; the painted snuffboxes, the oil paintings. One caught the eye instantly, both because of its size and its power; it dominated the room. Laura stared at it curiously. It had obviously been painted in the park, for the façade of Marston, gloriously sunlit, could be glimpsed in the background. But it was a portrait, dominated by its subject, a woman. She was casually dressed, wearing jodhpurs and an open-necked shirt. Her fair hair, cut boyishly short, was blown slightly across her face. She was slender and beautiful, the perfect oval of her features dominated by a wide mouth, and by eyes of an extraordinary piercing blue. She was looking out of the frame, her back to the house. In her hand she held a book; peering at it, Laura could just make out the words *Byron: Collected Poems* on its spine. The woman had beautiful long tapering hands, with pale oval nails, and one finger was inserted between the pages of the book, as if to mark a place of reference. Behind her, the park was empty, the sky unclouded, as clear and blue as her eyes.

Robert Wentworth straightened up, following her eyes.

'Lydia,' he said shortly. 'My brother's wife. This was her room.'

'She's very beautiful.'

'Yes, she was.' He turned back to the fire, just as it caught, sending a shower of bright sparks up into the darkness of the chimney. 'She's dead now. She and my brother were killed, in a car accident.'

Of course; as Mrs Grove's story came back to her, Laura stared at him curiously. His manner had changed totally since they came into the house. His gaiety, the debonaire nonchalance of lunchtime, had left him. Now he looked on edge, preoccupied, as if he were only half aware of her presence.

'So.' He made a visible effort to collect himself, turning back to face her across the room as behind him the fire began to blaze. 'Your advice. It's quite simple really. It's about this house . . .'

Laura stared at him. 'This house?'

'Yes.' He spoke abruptly. 'Would it be suitable for a child?' Seeing her look of incomprehension, he paused. 'A sick child. One that has been—still is—very ill?'

Laura looked at him blankly, a thousand questions instantly starting into her mind. When he didn't speak, she began hesitantly.

'Well, I don't know. It's very difficult to say. I should need to know more . . . of the circumstances. To see the other rooms . . .'

'But of course, I intend that.' He crossed quickly towards her and sat down beside her on the sofa, his movements suddenly decisive. 'I should explain.' The dark eyes met hers, and in them now was a closed, barred expression Laura had not glimpsed before. 'My brother and his wife were killed last year. They were visiting me, as it happened—in New Mexico. I was on location with this film, we'd just started.' He paused. 'They had a son, Alex. He was in the back of the car when it happened. He was five then; now he's almost six.' Seeing her look of sympathy, he hesitated, then went on, 'Alex was thrown out of the car. He was not badly hurt—or so the doctors tell me. Mild concussion, that's all. There's nothing physically wrong with him. The car was found almost immediately; he was taken straight to hospital. He's had the finest medical treatment . . .' He broke off and made an odd gesture as if warding off pain, and Laura's heart went out to him. 'He's physically unmarked by the accident. But he hasn't spoken since it happened.' His voice broke as their eyes met. 'Nothing—not one word. He functions perfectly normally. He can walk, move around . . . there's no motor damage, the doctors say, no medical explanation other than acute trauma. But he won't speak.'

Laura stared at him; her skin had gone cold.

'Where is he now?' she asked.

'Still in New Mexico. I've rented a special house; there's round-the-clock nursing staff. The doctors thought it best for him to stay there, so they could keep him under observation. The climate's good—there's a beautiful garden, a pool, all the toys he could wish for. A speech therapist comes in; he's had every test under the sun. He's seen more specialists than you would believe possible . . . and still nothing.' He looked at her brokenly. 'And so, I thought, perhaps it was the place. Perhaps if I brought him back here . . .' He broke off with an exclamation of anger. 'He's perfectly alert, you see. You can see it in his eyes. He watches everything—I swear he understands. But he won't speak.'

There was a silence. Laura forced herself to sound unemotional, practical, though she longed to be warmer and more comforting.

'If you brought him here, you thought it might unlock something? Help heal the pain?'

'Something like that. When he was here—before—he loved the place.' He shrugged, looking away hopelessly. 'It's probably a mad idea. The doctors aren't hopeful. They're giving up. I can tell. But I won't give up!' He turned back to her fiercely. 'I refuse to. I've cancelled all my arrangements after this film, pulled out of all my contracts. I've got a few weeks still to complete—we're on schedule. I could bring him back here, and be with him, for the spring, the summer, maybe longer. I thought—you know, an English summer . . . in the country . . .' The look of pain in his eyes as he turned back to her was so acute that Laura wanted to reach for his hand. She just managed to stop herself.

'Do the doctors positively object?'

'They don't positively do anything,' he said savagely. 'They hedge their bets. It couldn't do any harm. It might do some good. You can imagine the sort of thing.'

Laura nodded silently; she could, only too well. It had been much the same with her father. She stood up.

'Show me the rooms,' she said.

'All right.' He stood up without another word, and led the way out of the room. Together they walked silently up the great staircase, while Laura looked curiously around her, her mind still trying to take in all he had told her. It was all spotlessly clean; yet curiously unlived in, as if it had been empty many years. On the gallery landing tall windows looked out over the park; a lake glinted in the distance. The sun had come out again, and its light slanted in patches on the floor. It was a beautiful house, she thought, her courage suddenly returning to her. As soon as the light changed, its atmosphere became warm. All it needed was habitation, the sound of voices and footsteps—animals perhaps, flowers—so it became human.

Robert paused and then threw back a door off the east landing. 'This was our old nursery. Alex used it when he was here before his parents died; the night nursery is through there . . .'

It was perfect, she thought, her heart lifting. Any child would rejoice in rooms such as these. It was, in fact, an old-fashioned and charming nursery suite. There were two bedrooms, a bathroom, a small cosy sitting room, and an enormous playroom. All had an atmosphere of tranquillity and peace, as if generations of children had lived and slept in these rooms. They were bright, filled with light. In the playroom were shelves filled with picture and story books; there was an old wooden rocking horse with a moulting mane; pictures of birds and animals, boxes of toys, a train set. On the window seat, in a solemn row, was a line of elderly teddy bears, ranging from large and portly to small and much worn.

She turned to Robert Wentworth, her face alight with pleasure. Then she hesitated. Something like hope had come into his eyes as he watched her. She mustn't let her enthusiasm run away with her, she thought carefully. Consciously she checked herself.

'Well, obviously I'm not qualified to make a medical judgment . . .'

'I've had enough medical judgments to last me a lifetime. I want to know your instincts.' He took a step towards her. 'Please, Laura.' He stopped and gave her a wry smile. 'I trust your instincts, you see.'

'I don't know why you should . . . I'm very inexperienced . . .'

'Never mind why. I do.' He had come to a halt a few feet away from her, and was looking down into her upturned face. Under that dark intent gaze she felt herself tremble a little.

'Obviously he's not making progress where he is. And if the

doctors have no specific objections, then I think you should try it. Yes.' As she said the words, she suddenly felt a curious and sudden certainty, a conviction partly in her heart, partly from outside her, almost as if the room, the house, willed her answer.

Gently, formally Robert took her hand.

'Then there's only one other thing I want to ask you.' He paused. 'I want you to look after him.'

'Me?' She stared at him, her mouth suddenly dry, incapable of movement.

'Yes, you. I want you to come out to New Mexico and see him there, then come back with us, look after him here. That's what I want.'

'But . . .'

His grip on her hand tightened. 'You're free to do so now. You're leaving Zara's.'

'But I'm not qualified. I'm not experienced enough.' She stared at him wide-eyed, mesmerised by the force of conviction that blazed in his face. 'He would need a nurse, a proper nurse . . .'

'He can have a nurse—as many as you like. But that's not what he needs.' He paused, looking down into her face, his own suddenly gentle. 'He needs you, what I think you could give him.'

'And what's that?'

'Love, caring, patience—tenacity.' He paused, his eyes darkening. 'Youth, perhaps,' he said in a curious tone of voice, shaded with bitterness, 'and the optimism of youth. I could give him the other things, perhaps. But not that.'

There was a long silence; still he held her by the hand. Laura's mind whirled. Every instinct in her body told her to say yes, at once, without hesitation. But her mind cautioned her.

'I . . . I don't know . . .'

'Supposing I said,' he let go her hand, 'that it wasn't just Alex. That *I* needed you, to do this. What would you say then?'

'Oh, in *that* case . . .' She smiled. 'Since you obviously find it so difficult to admit, I should probably say yes.'

'Laura . . .' He made an impulsive gesture towards her, and for one absurd moment, seeing the joy come into his face, she thought he was going to take her into his arms. But instantly he checked himself.

'It would mean a great deal to me if you would. I have instincts too, you know. And from the first moment I saw you with Zara's baby . . .' He broke off, checking his tongue. 'I felt a kind of hope—the first hope I've felt for months.' He paused, and she saw the mockery light his eyes. 'So—you can organise everything as you see fit. I'll bow to your judgment. Just tell me what you need, what you want me to pay you, and . . .'

'It's not that.' She stopped him gently. 'There's only one problem. I'd have to tell Zara, and I'd have to say goodbye properly to her children. I might not be able to leave absolutely immediately. She said she wanted me to go, but I couldn't just walk out on them.' She shrugged. 'Apart from that, it's simple. I have no ties.'

'You mean you'll come? Just like that?'

'Why not? If you're prepared to trust my instincts, why shouldn't I?'

'Laura!' He took her hand again, and raised it lightly to his lips. Then he stepped back, his eyes alive with happiness. 'Come back downstairs,' he said. 'It's cold up here. Come and sit by the fire. I'll just get some more logs in, then I'll make you some tea, and we'll discuss plans—all right?'

Back in the morning room he drew the curtains and switched on the lamps. He drew a chair up for her by the fire.

'You'll be all right? You're not nervous on your own?'

Laura laughed. 'Of course not.'

'The logs are in the stables—I'll be about ten minutes. O.K.?'

When he had gone Laura stretched back in the chair, warming her feet near the fire. Everything had happened so swiftly she could hardly take it in, and she wondered if Robert Wentworth had this effect on other people's lives, erupting into them, altering them so swiftly. She thought of the little boy Alex; of New Mexico, a place that was just a name on a map to her, and her heart lifted. How wonderful, she thought, if she could do something to help him. She thought of the accident, and shuddered involuntarily. Before it happened, before he was thrown out of the car—how much had he seen? How had he found out what had happened to his parents? There so many things she needed to know, she thought. So many questions she must ask Robert Wentworth. What did Alex look like? she wondered. Did he take after his father, or his mother? Instantly her eyes were drawn back to the portrait. As she looked at it she realised she didn't like it very much. It was brilliantly painted; it subject was beautiful. But there was something so dead about it, about that empty landscape, that bare sky. Why Byron? she wondered idly, and at that moment she heard the car.

Tyres crunched on the gravel; an engine cut out; a door slammed. Instantly she tensed. A moment later a bell rang, an old-fashioned bell, clanging loudly through the empty house, so Laura started. She hesitated, then got up, opening the door to the hall. It was in darkness; she had no idea where to find the light switch. As she paused, fumbling against the wall, the bell clanged again, making her heart jump. Suddenly she felt afraid; the memory of Sammy's stories sprang into her mind. Then, telling herself not to be absurd, that ghosts didn't ring doorbells, she pulled herself together, and opened the door. It was pushed back impatiently at once, there was a drift of sickly heavy scent; then Zara walked into the hall.

'So it's true, then. You are here!'

She pushed past Laura in the direction of the light, and strode into the morning room.

'Where's Robert?'

Reluctantly Laura followed her. 'He's just gone to fetch some logs for the fire. Then we were going to have tea. Then I was coming back.'

'How charming! How very cosy.' Zara had positioned herself in the centre of the room, her back to the fire, and her eyes swept Laura from head to foot.

'He said he wouldn't be long. He'll be back in about five minutes . . .'

'It's not Robert I want to see,' Zara cut her off, 'it's you. Just what in hell do you think you're playing at?'

Laura stared at her. Zara's face was white; two bright spots of colour stood out on her cheeks. She could never disguise her anger, and now she was shaking. Laura felt her own temper begin to rise.

'It is my day off . . .' she began.

'Shut up! I'm not interested in your excuses.' Zara paused, then suddenly laughed, an ugly, bitter high-pitched laugh. 'Well, I must say you have gall! First you doll yourself up like a French tart, then you make eyes at my dinner guests. Then, the moment my back's turned, you go waltzing off without so much as a by-your-leave. God, Robert really must be desperate!'

Laura's chin tilted, and she looked at Zara angrily.

'I'm not aware that I have to ask your permission about what I do in my own free time,' she said sharply. 'Particularly in the present circumstances.'

'The present circumstances?' Zara's eyes narrowed. 'I'm aware you're fired, thank God, but that hardly explains your presence here, does it? What are you playing at—the famous film star's ever-available groupie?'

'No, I'm not!' Laura stared at her hotly. 'Mr Wentworth wanted to talk to me about his nephew.'

Zara's eyes widened. 'About Alex? What business of yours is that?'

Laura sighed. 'He's asked me to look after him,' she said quietly. 'You might as well know now. And since I'm leaving you anyway . . .'

'You thought you'd worm your way in here! God, it's disgusting! Wait until Michael hears about this . . .' Zara's fists had clenched, her mouth was set in a jagged line. There was a silence, while the two women stared at each other across the room, then slowly Zara's expression changed. A little catlike smile played at her lips. 'Well,' she said briskly, 'I must admit you're a quick worker. I suppose my husband wasn't good enough for you? I mean, you'd tried that, hadn't you, Laura? But I suppose once you met Robert Wentworth you changed your mind. What a little fool! Do you really imagine a man like that would waste five minutes on a stupid uneducated little tart like you?'

The temptation to smack her across the face was almost insuperable; Laura's temper flared, but she forced herself not to move, to keep her voice even.

'I don't want to listen to any more of this,' she said. 'Why don't you go, Zara?'

'Oh, I will.' Zara moved towards her, then paused. 'But I'll just tell you one thing before you go, just in case Robert forgot to mention it. You know who Alex is, don't you, Laura?'

The malevolence in her voice was such that Laura instinctively drew back.

'He's Robert's son, not his nephew. And if you think about that it might explain quite a lot, don't you think?' Zara laughed. 'There's only ever been one woman in Robert Wentworth's life, unfortunately. He was crazy about her when she was alive, and he's still crazy about her now she's dead.

And for years his poor dear stupid brother never even knew
what was going on under his own eyes.' She laughed, and
swung round suddenly to the portrait. 'She was lovely, wasn't
she? And you won't lay that particular ghost, Laura, don't
imagine it. Plenty of women have tried, believe me, but her
claws went much too deep. So . . .' she turned back, 'how do
you feel about it now? Looking after that pathetic little brat?
Not much point, is there really, when you won't make any
headway with his father?'

Laura stared at her, her face white; she knew she was
shaking with anger.

'There's plenty of point,' she said fiercely. 'Not that you'd
understand. The child is ill. His parentage isn't my affair, not
one way or the other. And nothing you could say would be
likely to influence me. So I suggest you get out, now. Unless
you'd like to stay and repeat what you just said to Mr
Wentworth . . .'

'Oh, aren't we fierce?' Zara pushed by her contemptuously.
'I'm going, don't worry. I'd hate to spoil your little tête-à-
tête—particularly now. After all, Robert's a man, like any
other. You never know your luck. He might think you were
just worth a one-night stand. But you'll know now, won't
you, Laura, who he'll be thinking of if he ever touches you?'
Before Laura could say anything, she had disappeared into
the darkness of the hall. 'Oh, and by the way,' she called back
mockingly over her shoulder, 'don't try coming back to our
house again, will you? I'd hate to have to slam the door in
your face. I'll get your things sent over tomorrow. I'm sure
you'll find somewhere to stay tonight. And you've got plenty
to think about now, haven't you?' She laughed; then the door
banged shut behind her.

Laura stood quite still; outside the car revved, tyres scrunched
on gravel; gradually the sound of its engine faded. She
listened to the silence. Outside, in the park, an owl hooted.
She thought: if it's true, I wish he'd told me. Then,
impatiently, she dismissed that thought. Her mouth set in an
obstinate line: it made no difference, she thought. If anything
her knowledge only increased her determination. I *shall* help
him, she said silently to herself, not quite certain, even as she
made the resolve, whether she meant Alex, or the man who
might be his father.

At the back of the house a door slammed. Seconds later

Robert Wentworth came into the room, his hair dishevelled by the wind, his arms full of logs.

'Sorry,' he said. 'They hadn't been split, so it took a bit longer than I thought.' He tossed them into a deep basket by the fire. 'Did I hear a car?' He turned, seeing her face for the first time. 'Laura?' He crossed quickly to her side. 'What's wrong?'

She forced herself to smile. 'You did hear a car. It was Zara.'

'Zara? What the hell did she want?'

Laura shrugged. 'Not much. She wasn't very pleased at the way I'd spent my day off. So she came to tell me not to darken her door again.'

'You're joking!'

'I'm afraid not; she's sending my things over in the morning. So as of tonight it rather looks as if I'm homeless.'

'But why?' He frowned. 'I don't understand. The damned woman's just fired you. Why the hell should she care one way or another?'

'I don't know.' Laura shrugged tiredly. 'She loathes me—I don't know why. She always has.'

'I can imagine.' He looked at her gravely.

She met his eyes. 'It doesn't matter. There's no point in making it any worse. I don't care, apart from the children, and she wouldn't let me see them anyway. So . . .' she paused, suddenly awkward. 'I think there's a pub near Ilmington that has rooms. Mrs Grove mentioned it once. It's the nearest. If you could take me over, I could stay there until . . .'

'You'll do no such thing. Don't be ridiculous! You'll stay here.'

'No, please—I couldn't do that.' She stared at him, feeling herself start to blush immediately. He smiled.

'You're not worried about the proprieties, I hope?'

'No, of course not! It's just that . . .'

'Then no more argument. You'll stay here tonight. I'll get your things in the morning, and tomorrow we'll go to London. We can fly out the day after.'

'But . . .'

'No buts and no blushes. It's decided.' He reached his hand up and very gently touched her face. Instantly he withdrew it, as Laura flinched. The casual fleeting contact of his fingers soared through her blood like a shock. Robert met her eyes levelly. 'You're not going to argue, I hope? You don't know me very well yet. I'm a very determined man, Laura. When I know I'm right about something, I always get my own way.'

In spite of herself, she smiled. 'Yes, I can imagine that,' she said.

'Good,' he said drily. 'Then that should save quite a lot of misunderstandings. Now, you'd better have my room, because none of the others has been used for months, and they're as cold as charity. I'll go and change the sheets—you can go into the kitchen and decide what to cook us for supper. And we'll have it in here, by the fire, just the two of us, and make plans. All right?'

'No, please. I can sleep down here. You mustn't . . .'

'No arguments, woman! You'll find the kitchen through the passage at the back of the hall. There's bacon and eggs. There might even be baked beans if we're lucky. Off you go!'

He pushed her firmly in the direction of the door.

Laura smiled to herself, opening the door to the huge kitchen. Suddenly her heart felt light; this was *fun*, she thought. He was fun. He made her laugh, and he made her feel alive and . . . She stopped, making a conscious effort to quell her own elation. It was dangerous to think like that; this was a job. Robert Wentworth was her employer. End of story, she said to herself firmly, and began to rummage around in the cupboards and the fridge.

Robert opened a bottle of white burgundy, and they drank it sitting on cushions by the fire, while he told her about Alex, about what it had been like before it all happened. He mentioned John, but never Lydia, but even that fact—and her awareness of it—did not affect their conversation. It felt easy, relaxed, warm; a special world, contained by the pools of lamplight, the heat of the fire. Then Laura cooked the bacon and eggs, and they ate them hungrily. When he had finished he put down his plate.

'Superb,' he said. 'The best meal ever. *Much* better than lunch.'

Laura laughed. 'You haven't had the pudding yet,' she said with mock seriousness.

'Tempt me.' He leaned back lazily, regarding her mockingly from under the long dark eyelashes that fringed his eyes.

'Rice pudding, tinned. Peaches, also tinned. Or jam if you prefer. Good nursery food, or it would be if it were home-made.'

He sat up with a jerk. 'You mean you can make proper rice pudding—the kind that's all crunchy round the edges, that you have with cream?'

'Certainly,' she laughed.

'You're a paragon! I knew you were.' His eyes met hers teasingly, and as Laura quickly got up, he reached for her hand.

'Don't be ridiculous. Men like you don't really like rice pudding.'

'What do they like, then?'

'Oh, I don't know.' She hesitated, the mocking flirta-tiousness of his tone making her deeply selfcon-scious. 'Sophisticated things. Crêpes, and sorbets. Amazing mousses . . .'

'Hate them.' His eyes met hers. 'I have very simple tastes.'

'Well, you'll be all right with tinned rice, then, won't you?' she said sweetly, and as he chuckled, she disengaged her hand.

They ate the rice pudding, then they sat companionably by the fire, sipping the somewhat bitter instant coffee Robert had made them, while he told her about New Mexico, about the film, about his co-stars.

'You'll like it there,' he said at last. 'It's very beautiful. Wonderfully hot. We can take Alex out in the car and . . .' he broke off, the look of pain returning instantly to his eyes. 'Goddammit, it's stupid, isn't it? I try and make plans, I start to feel hopeful again, and then . . .'

'Don't worry.' Laura leaned toward him gently. 'Don't think about it. Wait until we're there, and then we'll see.' She hesitated, frightened suddenly of sounding insensitive or banal. 'It doesn't do any good,' she finished, 'worrying about things when you have no way of affecting them.'

'Oh, but I can affect them.' He looked at her directly. 'I've found you. That's a start.'

'Not much of one.' She smiled at him wryly, anxious to divert him. 'You don't know what you're taking on. Why, I've only ever been in an aeroplane once. With my father we always went by sea. Sum total of flying experience—one school trip to Paris when I was fourteen.'

'Nonsense.' He smiled at her. 'You could cope with anything. It's one of the things I like about you.'

'Thanks a lot.' The compliment, if it was one, made her feel a little aggrieved. 'You make me sound frightful. Like some terribly efficient starched matron, with no imagination!'

'I said it was just one of the things,' he said lightly. Then, before she could answer, he levered himself to his feet, stretched lazily, and reached down to pull her up.

'It's late,' he said briskly. 'Past midnight—did you realise? We've a heavy day tomorrow, and you should get some sleep. Come on, I'll show you to your room.'

Silently Laura followed him as he ushered her through the door, and up the wide staircase. After the warmth of the fire the air was chilly; moonlight striped the stairs from the great windows. She shivered. Robert took her to what must have been the east wing of the house, near the nurseries. Finally, at the end of a corridor, he opened a door.

'In here. I hope you'll have everything you need.'

Laura followed him in nervously, looking around her. It was a beautiful room, the walls hung with the most exquisite hand-painted wallpaper, the furniture, deeply polished, gleaming in the light from the bedside lamp. But it was so evidently his room that she shrank from it instinctively. There were piles of books on the tables. On a table a case lay open; a shirt was tossed across the back of a chair. The bed, with its lace-trimmed sheets, was turned back. Resting on top of it, neatly folded, was a pair of black silk pyjamas. He saw her hesitation and laughed.

'Yes, well, I thought you wouldn't have a nightdress. They'll be far too large, of course, but it's the best I can do . . .' He gestured to the bathroom. 'Clean towels, masses of soap, and the ultimate intimacy—you get to share my toothbrush.'

'Look, please . . .' She stepped forward impulsively. 'I feel awful. Where are you going to sleep?'

He turned back to her, his eyes filled with mockery. 'On the sofa downstairs. It's warm there—perfectly comfortable.'

'But . . .'

'I thought we agreed. No arguments.'

'All right. But you shouldn't have gone to so much trouble. I . . .'

'Then I'll wish you goodnight. I'll call you in the morning. We should make an early start.'

'Fine. I . . . Thank you.'

He was about to turn away from her; just then, in the second she acknowledged to herself that the sudden sharp regret she felt was at his leaving, the wind outside gusted, rattling the windowpanes. From the park the owl gave its hunting shriek, very loud. She started, paling, and Robert turned back to her. Before she could move, before she could think, his arms came tightly around her.

'Laura ...' he said, his voice suddenly roughened, and suddenly his mouth came down on hers. It was an angry kiss, harsh and ungentle, with an edge of desperation that obliterated all her thoughts. She felt her body sag, resistless, against his chest, heard the thud of his heart against her. Her eyes closed; she knew nothing but his kiss. Want for him so sharp it terrified her, so immediate it must already have been lodged in her, waiting, unacknowledged, for this moment and this touch, arced through her body like a current.

She knew her lips parted; felt her arms reach up to him; he broke off the kiss and drew back abruptly. He held her, gently, at arm's length, and they stood there silently, his breath coming quickly.

Then, almost formally, he bent his head and brushed his lips against her forehead, tilted her face so she had to meet his eyes.

'Laura,' he said softly, 'I'm sorry. I can imagine what you're thinking. I shouldn't have done that. I give you my word, I'll never do it again. Think of it as an aberration, will you?' He laughed shortly, with an edge of bitterness that puzzled her. 'I have no wish to take advantage of you. I'm not like Michael.' His voice was harsh. 'In spite of what you must think. Put it down to the owl, and my chivalrous instincts. And don't look scared again—it's much too tempting! Goodnight.'

'Goodnight,' she said. But he had already closed the door.

When he had gone she thought of Lydia, and what Zara had said, and for a moment she felt a sharp bitter pain. Deliberately trying to keep her mind a blank, she washed. Then, wearily, she put on his pyjamas. Immediately she felt better. The silk was soft against her skin; the monogrammed pocket was over her heart. They were *his*, she thought, and hugged them to her. She didn't know why he had kissed her, but she would do as he said, and forget it. Still, he felt close to her, he would be close to her, for some time at least. She would be able to talk to him, and see him, and think of him. And maybe help him, she said to herself as she climbed into his bed. And his son.

CHAPTER FIVE

'WE'LL be in Albuquerque in an hour. The car will pick us up from there. But it's quite a long drive. Why don't you try to sleep?'

Robert leaned toward her solicitously, and Laura nodded obediently, closing her eyes. It was light outside the plane; she knew she would not sleep. Too much had happened, too fast; she wanted to think about it, prepare herself. They seemed to have been flying for ever, and she knew her body was tense with exhaustion. But still her mind raced.

He had woken her at eight, leaving coffee on a tray near the door.

'You're already dressed,' she had said accusingly, and he had laughed.

'Bathed, washed, changed—and still you never woke. The toothbrush is now all yours. I'm off to get your things from Zara's. Hope I get them all out of bed. I might make quite a scene, I think—I feel in just the mood.'

'Did you sleep well?'

'Abominably,' he said cheerfully. 'Not like you.' He shut the door, then opened it again, just as Laura was going to get out of bed. She shot back beneath the covers, and he gave her a hurt look. 'Relax,' he said 'I never break promises. Though I must say the pyjamas look much more fetching on you than me...however, I just wanted to check. You have a passport?'

'Yes,' she said weakly, wondering if he were always this energetic first thing in the morning.

'Good, then we'll pick up the visa in London. I've phoned the film company. They're fixing it, so it should be all ready. We don't want to waste hours at the Embassy. We've got to get you some clothes...'

He ducked out again, before she could answer him. When, later, in London, she had protested, he had turned to her with a cutting glance.

'Listen, woman. You go into this shop. It's supposed to be very good. Buy anything you like. If you don't like their stuff, we'll go somewhere else. And don't come out with one blouse, either. You need dresses—skirts—trousers. *I* don't know. A swimsuit—espadrilles, sandals. It's *hot* in New Mexico.

'But I can't . . .'

He gave her a threatening glance.

'Look, do you want me to come into the changing room with you and put them on myself? Because I will if you go on with this foolishness.'

'But I . . .'

'Right!' He gripped her arm firmly and marched her into the shop. The three assistants gaped, one—forgetting her elegant air of sophistication altogether—asked him for his autograph. He gave it, and then began pulling things off rails. 'This—and this. That's wonderful. Try that on.'

He held out a dress made of white silk chiffon. It had the lowest neckline and the highest price tag Laura had ever seen. She felt faint.

'No, please, you mustn't . . .'

'Right, if that's the way you want it . . .' He began to march towards the tiny changing booth at the back of the shop, towing Laura determinedly after him. Quickly she had disengaged herself, and ducked behind the curtain. She came out clutching one blouse and one skirt, chosen because they were the cheapest, not because she liked them the best. Robert was standing surrounded by the three assistants, who had apparently abandoned her for good. He was being, she thought, disgustingly charming. When he saw what she was holding he raised his eyes heavenward.

'What size is Miss Kent?'

'A perfect ten, Mr Wentworth.'

'Right. Then we'll take this, and this, and the white dress. And this . . . that's a swimming costume?' He held up a tiny backless scrap of shiny black Lycra. The assistants giggled as he raised his eyebrows. 'It's indecent, we'll take it.' Laura had stared in disbelief and mounting dismay, as he piled more and more things on the counter. Then he looked at his watch. 'Fine, just send them round to the suite at Claridges, will you?' He took Laura's arm. 'We must hurry. There's a couple of places in Beauchamp Place we should go to, one in the Fulham Road, and we might just have time to fit in Brown's in South Molton Street on the way to the Embassy . . .'

Out in the sunlight of Sloane Street, Laura stopped him, her mouth set obstinately. 'I can't accept this,' she said firmly.

He turned to her with a glance that made her pulse race.

'Do you want me to put you over my knee here and now and spank you? Because I will, you know. This is your uniform. Now be quiet!'

After that she gave up, and enjoyed herself. The day passed in a whirl. In and out of the Mercedes, parked with total disregard on double yellow lines. Into one shop after another.

'How do you *know* about all these places?' she asked finally in stupefaction.

'Didn't you know? *Vogue* is my book at bedtime,' Robert had said lightly.

She knew instantly that of course that was not true; it was Lydia who had told him. It was the only thing that clouded a perfect day. They ate oysters standing up in a bar in Jermyn Street; went into the American Embassy by a special door, and came out with the visa five minutes later; had tea and cucumber sandwiches in the Connaught, and then went back to the rooms he had booked at Claridges, to rest before dinner.

'I thought you said you were a man of simple tastes,' Laura said wryly, as she surveyed the piles of boxes sent up to her room, the Vuitton suitcases that had appeared miraculously to contain it all.

'I'm only interested in the best,' he said drily. 'And the best is always simple. I'll come and fetch you at seven. Please be ready.'

She was, and he took her, not as she had been expecting to some famous restaurant, but to a tiny Chinese place, tucked away in the depths of dockland, overlooking the reaches of the Thames. It was patronised excusively by Chinese, the owners knew him, and they had the most delicious meal Laura had ever eaten. When they had finished, Robert smiled.

'You see?' he said. 'I told you you were a paragon. Any woman who can eat cracked crab and ginger with chopsticks has passed the ultimate test.'

'Ah,' she said lightly, 'I'm a woman of accomplishments.'

'So I've gathered,' he replied drily, and from the expression in his eyes Laura thought she knew quite well to which accomplishment he referred. Instantly, as his dark teasing eyes met hers, the memory of his touch, of his kiss, pulsed through her body. She blushed deeply, furious with herself, and he laughed.

'Home,' he said, 'and plenty of sleep. We've more than ten hours of flying tomorrow.'

It was now nearer twelve, she thought, looking at her watch, though she had lost all track of time. They had been delayed at Heathrow; delayed again when the plane had had to stack at Kennedy, where they had transferred to an internal flight. In England, it must be about three in the morning, yet they were flying into the American sunset. She gave a little yawn, and snuggled back more comfortably into the airline seat. When she opened her eyes again, Robert was looking at her.

'Happy?' he asked.

'Yes, I am.'

'Funny. So am I.'

He laid his hand on hers, gently, resting it on the arm between them. She felt a moment's consternation, then a wonderful flood of peace and contentment. She fell asleep. His hand still covered hers when, a short while later, she woke. The plane had landed; they were about to disembark.

A huge sleek black Lincoln Continental was waiting for them. Diverted through the VIP route, it took only minutes to clear the airport formalities. Laura had a second, outside, to feel warm dry air against her skin, to hear the crackle of cicadas, to have an impression, made sharp by exhaustion, of palms, banked shrubs in flower, short coarse turf being watered by sprinklers, of crisp American voices, and the flash of cameras in their direction. On the horizon the tall white buildings of Albuquerque pointed against the huge bowl of the darkening sky. Then they were inside the car; the chauffeur had slammed the doors, and they were away. She leaned back on the wide, thickly upholstered seat, drawing her thin linen jacket more tightly around her. Robert laughed.

'The car's air-conditioned,' he said. 'Are you cold? I'll get Winston to turn it off.'

He leaned across to the glass partition, opened it, and said something to the chauffeur. The man flicked a switch.

'Sure thing, Mr Wentworth.' His lined black face, reflected in the driving mirror, split into a grin. 'You want me to take the interstate, or the desert route?'

Robert glanced at her. 'The desert route. I think, please. Miss Kent has never been to New Mexico.'

The driver chuckled. 'Okay. Scenic route comin' *up*!' He spun the wheel, his palm flat on its rim, and the huge car responded instantly, gliding across the three lanes of the highway, and down a turning that led away from the lights of the city.

'Thanks, Winston.'

'You're welcome. Good to have you back, Mr Wentworth, sir.'

Robert smiled, and leaned back beside Laura.

'Welcome to the New World,' he said.

Laura laughed. 'I feel foreign already!'

'So you should. You are. Don't be taken in by the fact that they speak the same language—or approximately the same language. You're as foreign here as you would be in Greece or Spain. It's useful to remember, sometimes.'

She looked at him curiously. 'But you don't feel that, surely?'

'Me?' He looked away. 'Oh, I feel foreign everywhere.'

'Oh, come on,' she said lightly, seeing that odd closed expression suddenly shutter his face. 'You can't. Not in England. Not at Marston . . .'

'Especially at Marston.'

He had turned his face to the windows, though she had the impression he saw nothing of the streets beyond them, the thinning strip of low white houses, the flags and lights of gasoline stations, the flashing signs of drive-in restaurants. The quickness with which his moods changed disconcerted her always. Now, her senses jangled and alerted through lack of sleep, it frightened her. Looking at the dark averted profile, she felt a lurch of timidity and dismay. Four days ago she had never met him; now she was on the other side of the Atlantic, in a strange place, surrounded by strangers, here to do a job she felt suddenly inadequate to do. Panic gripped her, and although she said nothing, Robert seemed to sense it, because when he turned to her again it was as if he had made a conscious effort to break his own mood. He gave her an encouraging smile; his tenseness was erased. She thought, looking at him: I should never forget, he's an actor.

'It'll take us about an hour from here,' he said. 'We've almost cleared the city. If the light holds you'll see a little of the desert. It's very beautiful . . .' His voice tailed away, as if he too were suddenly aware of the distance he had brought her, the strangeness of it, the size of the task before them.

Laura cleared her throat.

'I'm sure I shall like it.'

'I hope you will. The house is a little remote, but there are people around all the time. I don't think you'll be lonely.'

'I never feel lonely,' she said, more bravely than she felt, and he smiled.

'No, I can imagine you don't. You're very lucky.'

There was a moment's silence, an awkwardness between them. Laura hesitated, suddenly selfconscious, wishing she could dispel the atmosphere of unease and tension that seemed to have sprung from nowhere.

'I wondered . . .' She hesitated. 'Does Alex know I'm coming? Will anyone have told him?'

'No. The doctors know—I wired them. And I spoke to Graham—he's the paediatrician—on the phone last night, after we got back. But I'll tell Alex. Tomorrow, I think. Then you can see him.'

'Is there . . . is there any change?'

'No.' He sighed. 'No change.'

'I wanted to ask you . . .'

'Yes?'

'Well, lots more things, of course. But I ought to know—about the accident.' She paused, willing herself to go on, seeing the shutters instantly come down in his eyes. 'Does he know his parents are dead?'

There was a long pause, and she saw his fine narrow hands clench slightly. When he spoke again, his voice was flat.

'Yes, he knows. At least, I told him. Since he doesn't speak, there's no knowing for certain whether he understood me. But I think—he understood.'

'I see.' She paused. 'I'm so sorry. It must have been terrible for you . . .'

He turned to her, his voice suddenly savage with pain, so she longed to reach out to him. 'Oh yes, he understood. He cried—silently.'

'Oh, God!' She felt her throat tighten, and knew tears came to her eyes as they were filling his: not caring any longer, she reached across and took his hand.

'Laura,' he said.

Outside the car a vacancy of dry earth lay all around them, the shapes of rock outcrops and cactus just perceptible in the darkening light.

As they sped forward, in silence, Laura felt a strange force bunch, gather, build in her heart until it flooded through her body. It was as if her pity and her will bonded into one assertion of spirit so strong it was like air in the lungs after a period of suffocation. *He will get well again*, she thought, neither knowing nor caring if the thought were a wish or a prophecy.

Robert did not speak again, and eventually she withdrew her hand. His eyes were closed, she saw, though she thought he did not sleep. Carefully she averted her eyes from the shadowed planes of his face, harsh even in repose, and gazed out into the dark. There were no lights now, except those of the powerful headlamps on the road ahead. It was like traversing space, not land, an endless journey through the dark. And at the end of it, a small boy, whom she had not seen, even in photographs. An unknown child; yet she felt he drew her with a power as immense as gravity.

After a long time the car slowed, turned, began to mount a narrow drive that twisted and turned between the shadows of trees and plants. Laura glimpsed lights, heard the crunch of tyres on gravel. Then they stopped, and a door was thrown back, there was a clamour of voices. Winston opened the car door for her, and, her limbs stiff with tiredness, she climbed out into air crisp and cool against the skin. There was the scent of flowers, and, looking up, catching her breath at its loveliness, she saw the sky dark and immense above them, its heavens sharp with the clarity of Western stars.

After that her impressions were muddled and confused by her tiredness. Dimly she was aware of a long, low white house, tiled floors, a succession of brilliantly lit rooms, of being introduced to a housekeeper in a blue uniform with a white linen collar, and a manservant who took their bags. The housekeeper was Winston's wife; she caught that. To Laura, in her exhaustion, she seemed immensely kind.

'I'm Cecilia,' she said, leading Laura up a flight of winding stairs. 'But you just call me Cissie, like all the folks round here. And if you want something, well now, you just holler, O.K.?' She threw back the door of a bedroom, watching Laura curiously. 'You like somethin' to eat,. honey? Mr Wentworth, he said you'd be feelin' pretty tired and pretty hungry. I fixed some cold cuts for you downstairs. Nothin' fancy. And some corn muffins. I made corn muffins this mornin', just the way Mr Wentworth likes them.'

Laura smiled. 'Thank you,' she said, 'but I'm not hungry. We had dinner on the plane, you see, and I'm not sure what the time is in England, but it feels like the middle of tomorrow.'

Cissie laughed. 'And right now all you want is some sleep, I'll bet. Well, that's just fine. I'll fix you a special breakfast in the mornin'. You like coffee, juice? Hashed potatoes? And eggs? How you like your eggs? Shirred? Fried? Sunny side up? Over easy?'

Laura stared at her in bewilderment, then laughed.

'Coffee, please,' she said. 'And orange juice would be lovely. And apart from that, I'll leave it up to you, Cissie. Whatever you bring, I promise I'll eat it.'

The housekeeper smiled, her teeth amazingly white against the blackness of her skin. 'You mind you do now, honey. You look like you could do with some feedin'. Why, you're just so pale and thin you look like you could vanish away in the air!'

As she turned away to the door, she almost collided with Robert Wentworth, who was, Laura realised, standing there watching them quietly.

'Don't you go worrying her now, Mr Wentworth,' she said firmly. 'She don't want no supper, just sleep. What you done to that child? She looks plain worn out!'

'Done to her?' He smiled. 'I've just whisked her halfway across the globe, Cissie, that's all. Even you can't altogether blame me for jetlag.'

Cissie chuckled. 'If the good Lord had meant us to fly, he'd have given us wings, for sure. Now I made you some corn muffins, Mr Wentworth, and I want them eaten . . .'

With a flick of her starched skirts she was out of the door and down the corridor. Robert gave Laura a rueful look.

'That was Cissie,' he said. 'A force of nature. I should have warned you.' He paused, his face suddenly becoming serious. 'Laura, I know you must be exhausted. But before I leave you, I thought . . . Would you like to see Alex? He's asleep now, of course, but we could just look in on him, very quietly.'

'Of course.' She straightened, suddenly nervous, now that the moment had come. 'I should like that very much.'

He took her arm lightly, formally, and led her from the room. They passed down a short corridor, then branched off towards what seemed to be the back of the house. The lights here were softer; it was very quiet.

He paused, finally, at a narrow wooden door, then tapped very lightly. Laura felt her throat constrict with nervousness. She clenched her hands, determined he should not see it. He opened the door softly, and they stepped into a cool white room. There was one small lamp burning, with a green shade. In its light, reading, sat a nurse in a white uniform. She looked up, a smile of welcome on her face, and put her finger to her lips, nodding across the expanse of the room to a small narrow bed. Following her gesture, Laura turned. Then she stopped, unable to move.

In the bed, under a white coverlet, lay a small boy. He was lying on his back, one thin arm resting on the covers, the other thrown back across the pillow. Across the room the gentle sound of his breathing reached her; she could just see the regular rise and fall of his chest under a pair of thin cotton pyjamas. She stared at him, and then, as the man motioned her forward, followed him hesitantly to the side of the bed. They stood there in silence, looking down into the child's upturned face, and Laura felt the blood rush to her heart.

The child's hair was thick and black, his brows straight. Under his eyes were faint smudges of blue, the only signs of stress or illness. His lashes were dark: in the peace of sleep they brushed the faint colour of his cheeks. He was exceptionally beautiful, although all children were beautiful in sleep, Laura thought. His features still had the unformed softness of the very young. Yet even so the likeness to the man by her side was uncanny, and immediately apparent. In that instant any doubt she might still have had as to the truth of Zara's story evaporated into the night. Alex: his son, she thought, and a sense of profound tenderness mixed with pain pierced her heart. She looked down at the boy quietly, hardly daring to breathe. Under his closed eyelids she could see the flicker of eye movement: he dreamed. She knew then she need not ask or guess the colour of his eyes. Like his father's, they would be black, like water in darkness. Of what did he dream? she wondered, and at last turned quietly away, her heart aching.

They tiptoed out, closed the door silently behind them. At the top of the stairs by her room Robert took her hand.

'He's so beautiful,' she said simply.

'Yes, he is.'

Their eyes met, and for a moment she saw him hesitate, as if he guessed that she knew.

But he said nothing. He bent, with a curious formality, over her hand.

'Until tomorrow, then,' he said. 'Please rest well. Oh—and Laura . . .' She turned. 'Thank you.'

He left her abruptly. In her room she unpacked her overnight case mechanically, hardly aware of what she was doing. Tiredness swept over her in waves. When, finally, she slipped between the cool linen sheets, and closed her eyes she knew Alex would come to her in her dreams. And he did so; but not speaking.

Cissie woke her by opening the curtains in her room, so that from a deep, almost drugged sleep she was startled by the warmth of sun on her face. She opened her eyes to a brilliancy of light that made her wince. Cissie laughed, as she yawned and stretched.

'Goodness, whatever time is it?'

'Ten-thirty, honey. I guess I don't need to ask if you slept well.'

She placed an enormous silver tray on the table at the bedside; the room was filled with the mouthwatering aroma of freshly brewed coffee. Cissie surveyed her, arms akimbo, as she struggled to sit up.

'Now, this is your breakfast, and I want it eaten, honey. All of it, you hear me? And you've no call to be worryin' yourself about the time, 'cause Mr Wentworth, he said you're to take things nice and easy. He's seein' the doctors right now, so he says you're to make yourself feel right at home. He'll be down around twelve, he says, so you just eat your breakfast, and rest awhile. Then I'll send one of the maids up to run you a good hot tub. You fancy a nice long soak in a hot tub? Kinda eases the muscles, I think.'

She lifted the heavy tray on to Laura's knees, and Laura looked at the spread before her in amazement.

'It looks wonderful,' she said. 'And I'm starving. Thank you, Cissie. Did you make all this?'

'Well now,' Cissie paused at the door, a broad grin on her features, 'I fixed the food. Mr Wentworth, he provided the trimmin's!'

As she closed the door, Laura looked back down at the tray. Laid across the lace cloth was a single red rose. She stared at it, touched its petals, wonderingly. Where did you get roses, she wondered, in the spring in New Mexico? Then she laughed, holding its fragrance against her skin. He could get anything, she thought, if he wanted it. The thought made her heart quicken.

A little later, as Cissie had promised, a young girl with dark

Mexican features tapped at the door and came in shyly. She ran the bath, and then, laughing at Laura's protestations with a flood of Spanish, insisted on unpacking all the suitcases, murmuring in delight as all the beautiful things bought in London were carefully unwrapped from their tissue paper.

It was all a little unreal, Laura thought, as she lay in the deep scented water. She couldn't get used to the idea of servants, of meals arriving on silver trays, and baths being run for you. But for the moment, she thought wryly, it was fun, while it lasted. Her room was so pretty, and so luxurious, the tiled floor covered with intricately woven rugs, the colours—blues and yellows—as vivid as the sky and the air beyond the windows. From the window she could see the gardens below. They seemed huge, winding away, half hidden down the rise on which the house was built. Beyond them she could just see the edge of the desert; a flat redness, the horizon ringed with mountains, the air already shimmering in the heat. From below, amidst thick greenery, she could hear the hiss of sprinklers. It was obviously hot outside already, but the air-conditioned room, with its astonishingly thick walls and small wide windows, was deliciously cool.

Feeling suddenly excited, expectant, longing to explore, she hurriedly opened the huge carved pine wardrobe. She selected one of the prettiest dresses Robert Wentworth had bought her. Made of the finest cotton, it was a clear perfect turquoise, with soft cap sleeves and a plain neckline, so her hair fell, startlingly dark and thick, against the colour. There were some espadrilles that matched the dress, and she put an old coral necklace of her own around her throat, then stood brushing her hair meditatively, thinking not of the girl reflected in the mirror—though the dress pleased her—but of the little boy she had seen last night, who had visited her so forcefully in her dreams.

She went outside for a while, and wandered around the gardens, admiring the strange plants, the groves of orange and lemon, the bougainvillea massed on the railings around the terrace. As the sun climbed it grew hot, and eventually she sat on the terrace, leaning back so the sun washed over her skin, and looking out across the strange forbidding landscape. The house was built on a high escarpment; below the red desert stretched away to the horizon, marked only by the black ribbon of the road they had taken the night before.

At twelve, Cissie came out, and brought her a long cool

orange drink, and the two of them stood and talked for a little. There was no sign of Robert Wentworth, and Laura began to feel nervous.

'Where does Alex normally have his lunch?' she asked finally.

'Up in his room, honey, with the nurse. Then they have him rest for a hour.' She smiled. 'Hey, you're plannin' somethin' . . . what you got on your mind?'

'Well . . .' Laura hesitated. 'You said we might have lunch out here, and it's so lovely, so warm. I just thought he might have it with us. Mr Wentworth won't be here all that often after today, he said, and so . . .'

'Why not?' Cissie grinned broadly. 'It ain't natural, a child bein' shut indoors like that, and all the while the sun outside here shinin'. You ask him, honey. I figure if you ask him, he'll say yes.'

Laura stood up; the two women's eyes met in a glance of mutual warmth and understanding.

'Cissie, tell me—what was Alex's favourite food? Before the accident?'

Cissie frowned. 'Well now, he liked french fries—what kid doesn't? And—I know—he liked my fried chicken, said it was real good.' Her face clouded momentarily. 'His mother didn't like him havin' that stuff, though.'

Laura smiled at her innocently.

'What were we going to have for lunch, Cissie?'

Cissie looked blank, then suddenly she laughed. 'I get you!' she said. 'Why, fried chicken, honey, what else?'

Without further words, she bustled off in the direction of the kitchen. Laura went on sitting, looking out over the landscape, trying to make plans, trying not to be nervous, when suddenly she heard a movement behind her. She swung round. The door on to the terrace had opened. Standing there was Robert. Next to him, holding back and clasping his hand, was Alex.

There was a moment's silence while all three looked at each other. Alex was wearing English clothes: shorts, a white sports shirt. He looked painfully thin, she thought, and his skin was untanned. His eyes, wide in the delicate face, never left hers; they were black, and unwavering. Laura hesitated. She didn't want to rush him, and for once Robert seemed paralysed with indecision. So, slowly, taking her time, she got up and crossed to them. Not going too close to him, she bent and crouched down, so her face was on the boy's level. As she moved, he

flinched, and it took all her will power not to show her
nervousness.

'Hello, Alex,' she said. 'I'm Laura.'

There was silence. She had expected it, but even so it
unnerved her.

'Laura's come to be with you, Alex,' said Robert, his voice
strained. 'Won't you shake hands? She's come all the way
from England.'

The boy's eyes widened. There was a pause, then very stiffly
he held out his hand. Formally Laura took it and shook it, as
if he were a grown-up. His bones against her skin felt as fine
and fragile as a bird's. The hand was withdrawn instantly. He
did not smile. The moment she released his hand he edged
away, then ran to the end of the terrace, standing with his
back to them, his small hands gripping the railings of the
terrace.

Laura straightened up. She could see the doubt already
clear in Robert Wentworth's eyes, and she knew she must not
give him a second. She smiled at him widely, as if nothing had
happened. Alex's back was rigid, and she knew he was
listening to them.

'Isn't it a wonderful day?' she said lightly. 'I wondered,
could Alex have lunch with us outside today? Cissie said we
could have it here on the terrace, and she's making fried
chicken—she mentioned that Alex liked that . . .'

She knew her words had rushed out a little too quickly.
Even as she finished the sentence she saw a wicked gleam of
comprehension and amusement light Robert's dark eyes.

'Good idea,' he said, equally casually. 'I'm sure Alex would
like that. So should I!'

It was the most difficult meal she had ever had to get
through, nonetheless. She kept the conversation going, and
included Alex in it as far as was possible. Robert helped her—
so did Cissie who served them the meal, but it wasn't easy
sitting across the table, her every movement being closely
watched by two pairs of identical dark eyes. But she was
rewarded. Gradually, she could sense it, Alex began to relax a
little. He was still wary, but some of the tension seemed to
leave his body, and—after some hesitation—he ate well,
finishing all his fried chicken, and having two helpings of
Cissie's chocolate ice cream.

Towards the end of the meal she saw Robert glance
covertly at his watch, and she smiled at him.

'You have to go now, don't you?'

He sighed. 'I don't want to in the least. I'd much rather stay here with you and Alex, but I'll have to, I'm afraid. There's some test shots this afternoon, then we pick up the full schedule tomorrow. But I shouldn't be too long today. What will you do, do you think?'

'Oh, there's so many things!' Laura smiled at Alex. 'I want to explore the garden—I thought perhaps Alex might show me round. And there's a pool, isn't there? I'd love a swim later, if Alex would come with me. Do you like swimming, Alex?'

The boy turned to Robert with a look of mute enquiry.

'Alex loves swimming. He hasn't been in the pool for a while, but last time he did half a width. Would you like that, Alex?'

Alex gave a barely perceptible nod, but his lips lifted. Robert Wentworth stood up.

'Okay,' he said. 'We'll miss out on the rest, just for today and see how you get on, all right?'

'And we'll give you a full report when you get back. Maybe we could make it a width this time, what do you think, Alex?'

So, when Robert had left them, she and Alex explored the garden. At first he hung back shyly, then—as she had hoped—his child's natural exuberance began to reassert itself. He ran off ahead of her down the shady paths. He showed her a little tiled summerhouse, a tree with a long bent branch that was good to climb. Laura climbed it, hitching up her skirts, and after a pause, Alex scrambled up beside her. They sat there among the leaves looking out across the garden.

'You could have a tree-house here,' said Laura. 'Wouldn't that be good? When I was little I had some friends who had a tree-house—quite a big one, with a proper roof and everything. We used to go and hide up in it, and have picnics there . . .' She paused. 'I bet there's somewhere we could build a tree-house at Marston, don't you, Alex? Shall we try and do that, when we all go back there?'

The little boy nodded, his eyes wide.

The mention of Marston seemed not to upset him, and when they climbed down he allowed himself to be helped. Later, when Laura judged that their large lunch ought to be digested, they went back to the house and fetched swimming things. Then Alex led her down a winding path to where the swimming pool lay secluded from view among the trees.

'Right,' said Laura. 'I don't think we'll sink like a stone now, though you ate so much chicken, Alex, that I'm not sure.' She grinned at him, and again saw the flicker of response, the faint light of amusement in the watchful dark eyes. 'Now,' she swept him up gently into her arms, and very carefully held him so his feet dangled in the clear blue water. 'Ready to dive, Mr Submarine?' He nodded energetically. 'Batten the hatches, here we go!' She lowered him into the shallow water, then slid in beside him. It felt marvellous, intoxicatingly cool and refreshing, and for a while the two of them played in the shallow end, floating and splashing. He was quite confident in the water, Laura saw to her relief, and there was no sign of the tension earlier.

'Ready to swim that width now?'

Alex nodded.

'O.K. Take a deep breath—that'll buoy you up like a balloon. Come on, a really big one. That's it!'

Alex puffed up his chest, set his mouth, and launched himself, a look of grim concentration on his face. His thin arms, startling white in the sun, scrabbled through the water. His feet kicked wildly. About three-quarters of the way across, visibly losing his battle to stay afloat, he put his feet down and surfaced, spluttering.

'That was brilliant! Terrific! You nearly did it!' Laura clapped her hands. 'It'll be the Channel next, you see.'

Alex had a rest and then tried again.

'Very nearly, Alex! Remember, you don't have to fight the water, it'll hold you up if you relax. Try and breathe through your nose, and keep the arm movements steady, like this. Have a float, then try again . . .'

The third time, quite easily, he did it. He grabbed the rail on the far side, and gave an odd silent little gesture of triumph that made Laura's heart turn over with pity. Quickly and lightly she bent and kissed him, happy that he did not flinch from her, but—for the first time—took her hand, and just held it shyly.

'You see? I knew you could do it! That's terrific. We'll tell Uncle Robert as soon as he gets back, shall we? He'll be so proud . . . And tomorrow we might have a race—will you beat me, do you think? I think you might, Alex, I'll have to practice.'

Not wanting to overdo it on the first day, and tire him, she helped him out of the pool soon after, then lay down with him in the sun to dry off. She was beginning to get used to the fact that he did not speak; she was used, in any case, to talking quite unselfconsciously to babies such as Jonathan, and Alex's concentration on her words, the response in his eyes, made up for the lack of answer.

So, companionably, they stayed by the pool. Laura talked about everything under the sun: her own childhood; Samantha and Jessy and the games they had all played last summer; the flight to New Mexico. At the mention of aeroplanes she saw his face lighten with interest. To her surprise, he bent down, and wetting his hand in the pool, drew the rough outline of a plane on the dry tiles beside her.

'That's very good, Alex,' she said, as he leaned back on his heels. 'Do you like drawing?'

He gave her one of his slight, just perceptible nods.

'Shall we do some pictures of them tomorrow? And maybe we could find you some books about aeroplanes, would you like that?'

Again the slight nod. Laura smiled, and jumped up.

'I know,' she said, 'watch this. I'm not sure if I can make it work, but let's try . . .'

There was a small changing-house by the pool, where she had noticed some old magazines. While Alex watched, she carefully tore out one of the pages and began folding it.

The first attempt was not a success; the paper was visibly plane-shaped but nose-dived instantly they tried to fly it. She tried again; this time, as she spread the paper, Alex reached across and pointed.

'Like that? Oh, I see, fold it there . . . that's it!'

She gave it to Alex. He held it carefully between thumb and forefinger, drew back his arm, and let it go. The paper plane flew in a clear arc almost the width of the pool. Now totally absorbed, Alex clapped his hands and trotted off and fetched it. He returned and handed it solemnly to Laura. She tried, and again it flew, not as well as the first time, but several feet. Alex's face lit up with a wide smile. He ran across and picked up the scrap of paper, then held it aloft over his head. Laura watched him as, squinting his eyes against the sun, he held it triumphantly aloft. Then she froze. Very softly, scarcely audible, came a sound. She stared in amazement. It was a familiar enough one, the sound of a child imitating a plane's engine. And it was Alex who was making it. He repeated it, twice, perhaps three times, a low soft crooning, then he launched the plane. Then there was silence again. For a moment Laura thought she must have imagined it; then she knew she had not. She felt tears prick her eyes and turned quickly away, so that Alex should not see them, but her heart lifted with hope.

It was then, as she turned away, that she saw the man. He was standing on the other side of the pool, in the shade of some trees, watching them. Instantly she stiffened. Who was he? Why was he there?

As she stood up the man smiled, and strolled towards them. He was tall, blond and bearded, wearing a white open-necked shirt, blue jeans, and sneakers. Around his tanned throat was a chain with a medallion; silver and blue, it glinted in the sun. Alex had seen him now too; he stopped launching the plane, and just stood there watching the man come towards them.

'Hi, Alex.' The man raised a hand in casual greeting. He turned to Laura, and she saw a pair of frank blue eyes take in at a glance the skimpy black Lycra swimsuit, her slender figure. 'And you must be Laura, I guess.' He had registered her embarrassment, and it seemed to amuse him. 'I'm Tony Graham. Cissie told me I'd find you two down here.'

'Doctor Graham?' Laura stared at him. He was not in the least as she had imagined, and much younger than she had expected.

'That's me.' He grinned, and reached across to rumple Alex's hair. 'How you doin'? Skipped your rest this afternoon, huh?'

Alex gave him a sheepish smile, and the man laughed. Without more ceremony he lowered himself on to the tiles by Laura's chair and stretched out in the sun. Alex hesitated, then went back to playing with the paper plane.

'I don't think it's done him any harm,' Laura began defensively when he was out of earshot. 'I mean missing his rest. He doesn't seem tired, and he enjoyed it in the pool, and . . .'

'Hey, slow down! No criticism implied.' He smiled at her. 'Alex looks just fine—best I've seen him for weeks. What's the secret?'

Laura hesitated, then sat down, looking into the man's wide freckled face, and finding she instinctively liked him.

'Well,' she said, 'obviously I hardly know Alex yet. I haven't really had time to . . . to find out much about his illness. So I thought the best thing would be to keep things as normal as possible. Just let him enjoy himself, like any child. Get him to relax, to begin to trust me . . .'

He was regarding her intently, and her voice tailed away.

'Sounds fine to me. Just what the M.D. ordered.' He paused. 'Robert didn't get around to telling me too much about you, Laura. He kinda sprang you on us a bit, but then I guess that's the way he operates. Have you done much therapy with kids—I don't mean kids like Alex, of course, but autistics, anything like that?'

Laura's eyes widened. 'No, nothing like that.' She hesitated, then decided she might as well be honest. 'I'm not trained in that way, you see. I'm a nanny. I know very little about child therapy. I just thought maybe the best therapy for Alex might be attention. And love.'

To her surprise the man threw back his head and gave a deep throaty laugh.

'Just like that, huh?'

Laura met his eyes levelly.

'Yes,' she said firmly, 'just like that.'

He leaned forward to her. 'Let me tell you, I think you're quite right. And you're talking about two things that kid has been missin' out on for some time.'

Laura stared at him. 'You mean since the accident?'

'Since the accident and before the accident.' He spoke firmly, and met her eyes directly. Laura knew she flushed with colour. 'Listen, Laura. What Alex needs is a mother.' He jerked his head in the child's direction, where, out of hearing, he played contentedly by the pool. 'What you need to realise is that's nothing new. I reckon Alex has needed a mother a long time—a really long time.'

Laura stared at him. Instantly the portrait of Lydia sprang into her mind: that tall beautiful woman, with her eyes the same colour as the wide empty blue sky.

'You mean—Lydia?'

'Who else?' He shrugged. 'Robert knows what I think, so I guess I'm not speaking out of turn. You'll never get him to admit it, of course. But I met Lydia a couple of times out here, before it happened. And—well, let's just say she didn't strike me as exactly mother nature.'

Laura lowered her eyes. 'She . . . she was very beautiful,' she said slowly.

He laughed softly. 'Beautiful? Oh, sure. So are icebergs, of course.'

There was a brief tense silence. Laura looked across the pool at where Alex was still playing. She hesitated, and then turned back to the man beside her.

'You're trying to tell me something,' she said finally, meeting his frank blue-eyed gaze. 'Why not come out and say whatever it is you want to say?'

'O.K.' He met her gaze levelly. 'Just bear in mind that Alex's problems don't seem to me to stem from the accident alone. They could do. Shock, trauma—it all explains it very neatly. But I have the feeling it's something more than that.'

'Tell me.' Laura leaned forward, lowering her voice. 'There's one thing I ought to know, and I didn't like to ask Mr Wentworth. Is it known . . . could Alex have witnessed the accident? Been conscious at the time? Could that account for all this?'

'It's possible he was.' He hesitated, looking down at his hands and lacing his fingers together, as if unwilling, now, to meet her gaze. 'I kind of doubt it. It must have happened pretty fast. Alex had concussion, and he didn't come round till he was in the hospital. So I doubt he saw anything— anything he'd remember.' He shrugged and looked away. 'Though it wasn't a pretty sight. It took three hours to cut them out. It's a miracle the kid's alive.'

Laura stared at him in bewilderment. 'But then I don't see what you mean,' she said. 'If it wasn't that, if it wasn't the shock, what could it be? I mean, Alex was normal before the accident, wasn't he?'

There was a pause, and their eyes met.

'Yeah, *he* was normal. He was cute, a really bright kid. I liked him a lot.'

He stood up abruptly, as he saw her face cloud at the odd emphasis of his words.

'Let's leave it there, shall we, Laura? Just one piece of advice. I'd stay off the subject of parents. You know—no questions, no attempts to jog his memories on that score, right?'

Laura stood up too. 'I wouldn't dream . . .' she began stiffly.

Tony Graham laughed. 'Look, stop bein' so damn prickly, will you? It's just a suggestion, that's all. You keep on the way you've been doin'. That way you'll be good for Alex, good for Robert, and good for me. So, have we got ourselves a bargain?'

Laura laughed. 'No bargain, but I'll do my best. And now I'd better get changed, before I start asking a paediatrician to treat me for sunburn! I'm not used to this heat.'

'Glad to oblige any time, lady,' he drawled, his eyes unapologetically raking her from head to foot.

She turned quickly away, embarrassed by the frank admiration in his eyes.

'Shall we see you back at the house?' She turned to the small changing-room, as Alex came running over to her side.

'Nope.' He grinned. 'I'll walk you right back there. *If* you'll permit me. That O.K. with you, Alex?'

And, since Alex of course said nothing, and Laura didn't like to demur, he did just that. He waited for them to change, and then they walked up the path to the house together, Alex in high spirits now, skipping ahead of them with his paper plane, Laura and this man she had difficulty thinking of as a doctor, walking more slowly behind him, deep in conversation, as Tony Graham questioned her about England, and her work there.

'Yeah, well, I've got to say you surprised me.' He laughed and gave her a sideways glance. 'When Robert said he was bringing over some nanny I had it all weighed up—sixty-five, kind of plump, grey hair, starched apron. The full bit, you know . . .'

'Sorry to disappoint you.' Laura looked at him demurely.

'Who said anything about disappointment?'

His tone was now openly flirtatious, and Laura smiled to herself. Did he try that kind of line with most young nurses? she thought. And she had just decided that he probably did, and so would be unlikely to mind when she didn't respond— and though she liked him, she knew she wouldn't—when she saw Robert Wentworth.

CHAPTER SIX

HE was standing just above them on the terrace, a long iced drink in his hand, and an expression of cold distaste on his face. Quite clearly he had been watching them as they walked so unconcernedly up the path, and equally clearly he was not in a good temper. His mouth had set in a straight line; his brows knitted in a cold frown. She faltered, and in the same moment saw Alex rush to him, brandishing the paper aeroplane in the air, and plucking at his sleeve to attract his attention.

To her dismay he ignored Alex completely; instead his eyes never left her face. Hurriedly she quickened her pace, hastening up the flight of steps to join him.

'Hello,' she said nervously. 'We've been for a swim, Alex and I. It's been a lovely afternoon. Alex swam a whole width by himself, and we made a paper plane and . . .'

'So I see.' He cut her off coldly, meeting her eyes with an expression of such suppressed fury that she quailed. 'And you've met Graham, I also see.' As Tony Graham came bounding up the steps behind her, offering his hand, he took it with apparent dislike, so that the young doctor was brought up short in his tracks. There was a sudden awkward silence. Alex's eyes widened, and, her heart contracting with a sense of despair, Laura saw him almost visibly shrink back into himself. Suddenly his whole stance altered; his thin limbs tensed, the look of expectation and excitement faded from his face. His small hand dropped from his uncle's sleeve, and he backed off silently, hanging his head, the paper aeroplane drooping from his fingers. She saw an expression of confusion and concern flit across Tony Graham's features.

'Laura and I have just been getting ourselves acquainted,' he said awkwardly. 'I've been filling her in a bit, bringing her up to date on the case and so on . . .'

That wasn't exactly the truth, Laura thought. If what she'd just received was a medical briefing, it was a pretty unconventional one. Anyway, Robert Wentworth seemed to share her doubts.

'Oh really?' His eyes met those of the doctor in a cool arrogant stare. 'Well, that's very good of you, but I don't want to detain you.' He looked ostentatiously at his watch. 'It's getting late, and I'm sure you must have a lot of work back at the hospital . . .'

'Sure.' Tony Graham took the obvious hint with good grace. He smiled easily. 'Well, nice to meet you, Laura. Keep up the good work, huh? I might look in tomorrow. See ya then, young feller. Robert . . .' He rumpled Alex's hair, then paused by Laura as he turned to go. 'Keep on with the treatment— the one you prescribed, right?' He grinned at her, then he was gone.

'Just what did that mean?' Robert was staring at her haughtily, and Laura felt her temper quicken. Whatever was the matter with him? she thought angrily. He was looking just the way he had when she first laid eyes on him at Zara's dinner party—bored, arrogant, and too damn sure of himself by half. Maybe something went wrong out on location, she thought quickly, as his eyes, dark and forbidding, met hers. And so what if it did? she thought rebelliously. He has no right to behave like this, not now, not to Alex, not to his . . .

'I haven't the least idea,' she said crisply. 'Would you excuse me? Alex missed his rest, as you know, and I think he's probably tired. Would you mind if I got some supper for him—and then he really ought to be in bed.'

'Of course.' His mouth tightened. 'Please don't let me distract you from your duties.'

Duties! She stared at him in disbelief. Alex had heard what he had said; his thin face had taken on a wan pinched look. Laura felt her heart fire with pity and anger. Thanks a lot, Mr Wentworth, she thought furiously, you've just undone with one word what it took a whole afternoon to build up! Using all her will power, she fought back the anger; she gave Alex an encouraging smile and a wink.

'Duties?' she said lightly. 'Cissie said she'd make us waffles and maple syrup. Eating them won't be a duty, it'll be a delight, won't it, Alex?'

Reaching instinctively for the boy's small hand, and feeling it instantly and reassuringly reach up for her own, she turned to the door.

'Well, don't eat too many of them,' Robert called after her, in a cold sarcastic voice. 'You might remember, you're having dinner with me.'

Laura stopped in her tracks, then recollected herself, and laughed as lightly as she could. 'No problem,' she called back over her shoulder. 'With all this swimming I've worked up an appetite for at least two dinners, maybe more!'

Cissie fussed over them, and cooked Alex an enormous supper. After the first few minutes, as Laura told Cissie about their afternoon, and the swimming triumphs, Alex seemed to recover his good spirits, and ate well. Laura managed to eat one waffle, for his sake, but the scene on the terrace had killed her appetite stone dead, and left her with a nervous apprehension that she could not shake off. But she managed to disguise it well enough, or hoped she did. Then, when he was tucked up in bed, she read him a story, while the night nurse hovered in the background, straightening the room.

'Would you like a teddy in bed with you, Alex?' His eyes widened. She saw him glance at the nurse, and then he nodded.

The toy animals had all been put away in a cupboard out of sight; quickly Laura found them, and laid them out in a row on the end of his bed.

'There now,' she said. 'You choose, Alex.'

He pointed to the oldest, smallest bear, one with torn ears and moulting fur, unhesitatingly. Laura caught it up, placed it in his arms, and gave him a quick kiss. He didn't return it, but he didn't turn away either.

'Goodnight, then,' she said gently, smiling down at him. 'Sweet dreams, and see you in the morning, O.K.?'

To her surprise, as she turned from the room, the nurse motioned her outside and shut the door so that Alex should not hear them. Her kind face looked at Laura with an expression of obvious embarrassment.

'I'm sorry, Miss Kent, but I just felt you ought to know. Mrs Wentworth, Alex's mother, she didn't like him taking anything to bed with him.'

'What?' Laura stared at her in astonishment, and the nurse lowered her eyes.

'She thought it wasn't good for children, I guess. That kind of dependency, you know?'

'Well, I'm sorry, but I don't agree. It's the most natural thing in the world, and there's absolutely no harm in it.' She had spoken a little sharply, but then guessing from her face that the nurse shared her feelings, she softened her tone. 'Please, leave things as they are for the moment, will you? I'll speak to Mr Wentworth about it. I'll explain that it was my decision.'

'Sure.' The nurse gave her a wide smile. 'And I'm real glad you're here, Miss Kent. Alex looks better already.'

Back in her room Laura paced back and forth, her body tense. Then she sat in front of the mirror, brushing her long thick hair with sharp angry strokes. She felt suddenly, furiously, protectively angry, and she knew the last thing she ought to do was face Robert Wentworth again when she was in this mood. If she saw him now, she knew she would speak sharply, question him as to why he had behaved so coldly to Alex and herself, confront him over the business of the teddy bear.

And that wasn't a wise idea, she thought, slowly putting down the brush. Things were not as simple, as straightforward as he had made them seem. Lydia might be dead, but obviously he still bowed to her wishes—even the idiotic, the heartless ones. The last thing she needed, for Alex's sake, was to turn this job into a confrontation between her own wishes and those of a woman he had idolised. Had he loved her, the way Zara had said? Was it true? Instantly the image of the woman in the portrait floated into her mind and fixed there, cold, blue-eyed, and now somehow malevolent. She gave a little involuntary shudder. It was as if, even here, Lydia reached out from the grave to touch her. She stood up abruptly, and moved restlessly around the room. She must shake off these thoughts, she told herself impatiently. If Robert was still obsessed with a dead woman, there was no reason she should be. It was not her affair. She must think of Alex; of the future, not the past.

She had been taken in, she thought, a little bitterly. Taken in by Robert Wentworth's apparent nonchalance, the sudden gaiety of which he was capable, by his infernally easy charm. And under that? Well, she had seen glimpses of that brooding darkness, and it frightened her. *Lost happiness and lasting pain*, the words came into her mind again, just as she reached the window that overlooked the terrace where he had been, and saw it empty. *Damn it*, she thought, turning away impatiently. He's not my concern; Alex is.

She took her time changing for dinner, trying to calm herself, wanting to make sure her temper had cooled. She chose a simple white dress which left her arms bare, and tied at the waist with a soft suede belt of brilliant scarlet. She put on flat red shoes that matched the belt, and then, nervously, looked at herself in the glass. Pleased with the dress and the shoes, she gave in to a sudden wave of gaiety and an odd excitement, and executed a little pirouette, laughing at her own foolishness. She thought: Right, now to confront the ogre!

But of course, when she came downstairs and found him outside on the terrace again, he too had had time to collect himself, and was an ogre no longer. He stood up as she arrived, and she saw his dark eyes travel over her from head to foot.

'Well,' he said finally, 'you've been a long time. But it was worth it.' He gave her his easy bewitching smile, though she thought she could still detect a glitter of suppressed anger in his eyes. 'You look like a Navajo princess. Here . . .' There were oleander and gardenia growing in earthenware pots on the terrace, and he bent and plucked one of the waxy white gardenias and tucked it into the long fall of her black hair. 'There.' He stepped back, as if to admire the effect. The fleeting touch of his fingers against her skin had startled and alarmed her; it passed like a current through her body, though she could see from his eyes that he mocked her.

'A Navajo princess,' he repeated. 'Or a Navajo bride.'

'Navajo?' she looked at him blankly and he laughed softly.

'Didn't you know, Laura? This is Navajo country. This house is built on the edge of their old hunting territories. It's filled with ghosts.'

He turned away for a second, his eyes travelling over the red horizon, the colour of blood in the setting sun. Darkness would fall soon. She shivered, for the air was growing cool. Ghosts. She did have a sense of ghosts in his presence, she realised it as he spoke. But not the ghosts of Navajo tribes.

'Let me get you a drink,' he said. His own glass, on one of the tables, was empty. He refilled it, pouring a large measure of some dark brown liquid like whisky into the tall glass. For a second Laura had the impression that he had been drinking since she had left him, quite heavily, although he gave no sign of its effects. And watching him steadily she recalled what he had said to her once, that night at Zara's. *I get drunk only when I want to.* Did he want to now? she wondered. And if so, why?

'Bourbon?' He tilted the bottle at her mockingly.

'I've never tried it.'

'Then try it now.' He poured an equally large measure into another glass, and added water and ice, though he drank his own, she saw, neat. 'Like it?'

Laura took a sip and nearly choked. She wrinkled her face in distaste.

'Not much.' She smiled, but there was no response.

'It gets better with the second glass.'

'And the third?' she asked quietly.

He laughed shortly. 'The sweetest glass is the one at the bottom of the bottle. Isn't that what they say?'

'You mean you like to get drunk?' She met his eyes levelly, astonished at her own daring.

'I like to forget—sometimes.' He tossed off the last of his drink and set down the glass abruptly.

'And bourbon helps you do that?' she queried steadily.

'Sometimes it does.' His voice was low, suddenly dark. He moved towards her slowly, until he was very close to her, looking down into her upturned face. 'Bourbon. Whisky. Women. Music. Driving too fast. They can all make one forget, for a while. Predictable panaceas, I'm afraid. Not original at all. None that you'd approve of, little Miss Nursery Nurse. You'd prescribe very different things, no doubt, wouldn't you? A regular regime, perhaps. Not too much excitement. Warm milk at bedtime—very cosy. Effective for a child, I'm sure, but not for a man.'

The sarcasm in his voice was vicious; it took all her will power not to flinch from him.

'I wouldn't prescribe whisky,' she said coldly, meeting his eyes. 'Or bourbon. Running away never solved anything.'

'Did it not? How infinitely sure of yourself you sound, how wise and how smug! You're twenty-two years old, and I'll tell you something for free. You don't know what the hell you're talking about.' He paused, his eyes glittering at her dangerously. 'Have you ever been drunk? Just once? Have you ever done anything in your cautious, careful well-ordered life just for the hell of it? On the spur of the moment, without adding up all the pros and cons like a goddamned computer? Have you, Laura? Have you?'

She felt the colour flush into her cheeks; hurt stabbed at her heart.

'I came here,' she said quietly.

'Oh yes, of course, you came here. So you did. To look after Alex. How very brave of you! You've taken a risk. So . . .' he reached out suddenly and gripped her hand painfully around her glass, 'take another, why don't you? Drink your bourbon.'

Laura felt her temper flare; her eyes flashed at him.

'You think I can't?'

'I think you won't.'

'All right, then.' She raised her glass, and as she did so he released her hand. She hesitated; it was stupid, she thought, to allow him to challenge her like this, as if they were engaged in some childish dare. Yet it didn't feel like a challenge; it felt like a test. I'll pass it, damn him, she thought defiantly, and slowly she drained the glass. She managed not to choke on it; the taste was unpleasant.

Robert stepped back, watching her, and when she finished the drink he shrugged.

'Right, shall we go in to dinner?'

'If you like.'

She followed him across the terrace, and as she stepped into the light from the room, he suddenly paused, looking down at her, and laughed.

'Red shoes,' he said, looking down at her feet.

'Yes?' She looked up at him uncertainly.

'Ah, too young—the generation gap. It was a rather unsuitable story for children, and a famous film.' He smiled at her mockingly. 'It's a simple story. The girl is given a pair of red shoes. When she has them on she can dance quite beautifully—more beautifully than anyone has ever danced then or since. There's only one difficulty . . .'

'And what is that?' Laura stared at him feeling the pulse begin to beat in her throat, held by the blackness and threat in his eyes.

'In the end, she can't take them off. She wants to. She wants to stop dancing. But she can't.'

'So . . . so what happens?' Her voice caught drily in her throat.

'Why, she goes mad, of course. And then she dies.' He was looking straight into her face, but she had the impression that he did not see her. It was as if his eyes, intent on her features, saw those of someone else. Lydia, she thought, and fear crept like water over her skin.

'You gave me these shoes,' she said. Her words seemed to recall him; he smiled.

'So I did,' he said softly. 'So I did.'

The exchange seemed to break the odd spell of the last few moments; certainly his manner and his mood changed when they sat down to dinner. As quickly as he had allowed it to appear, all coldness and threat left him; he was solicitous, charming, amusing, just as if the encounter on the terrace had never taken place, Laura thought, watching him. Yet her mind burned at the memory of his words, at the contempt he had shown her. *Actor*, she thought angrily, as he passed her food, poured her wine. *What are you playing at?* Yet some instinct, some sixth sense warned her; he might be playing now; he had not been then.

Still, as he plied her with the delicious food Cissie had cooked for them, and refilled her glass with a light greenish

wine, she felt her guard beginning to drop, her tenseness
dissipate. Robert drank his wine steadily, but not excessively,
and gradually she cast aside the suspicion that he had been
drinking earlier. There was no sign of the slightest
intoxication; just a measured politeness, a constant stream of
apparently concerned questions as to how she had passed the
afternoon.

'And you liked Graham?' he said casually, after she had
recounted their exploits by the pool.

'Oh yes,' she said eagerly, hoping to maintain the pleasant
intimacy of their conversation. 'He wasn't at all what I
expected. Much younger, and not like a doctor somehow. But
he was very kind . . . I'm sure he's very concerned for Alex.'

'For Alex?' One finger was tapping the table idly. 'Oh, I'm
sure he is. An excellent man.'

There was a touch of irony in his voice, but Laura decided
to ignore it and went rushing on. Now was the moment, she
thought. If she could only explain.

'Alex was so proud of what he'd done, you see,' she said
quickly. 'When we got back to the house, he was really
looking forward to your knowing he'd swum the width. That
we'd made the plane . . .' Her voice tailed away, under his
dark regard.

'Yes. And I disappointed him. Is that what you were going
to say?'

Laura hesitated, then spread her hands. 'I think a little,
yes.'

'I'm sorry.' His eyes grew serious. 'I was aware of what I'd·
done. It was my fault. I'll try to do better next time.' He
shrugged. 'I had something on my mind. You must forgive
me.'

'No, please, you mustn't apologise. I didn't mean to sound
critical. It's just that . . .' she hesitated. 'Well, obviously you're
very important to him—the one link with the past. He wants
your approval, your love. I know he has it, but he's so
insecure at the moment I think he's going to need constant
reassurance. Now that his mother is dead . . .' She broke off,
wishing she could bite back the words, knowing she had gone
scarlet. Robert watched her carefully.

'And his father,' he said at last, his voice even as steel.

'Yes. Yes, of course.' There was an appalling silence, which
seemed to Laura to go on for an eternity. When at last he
broke it his voice was measured, and careful.

'I wonder,' he said. 'You blush so easily, it's very charming. But I wonder why you should blush at the mention of Alex's parents?'

'I ... er ...' She drank a little wine, desperately trying to think of a way out. As she replaced the glass it came to her. 'It's just that I was reminded ... it's awkward and I don't want to seem interfering. But I gather Alex's mother didn't like him having toys in bed at night. I gave him one, you see, and the nurse mentioned it. I wanted to ask you if ... if I might change that.'

'Oh, I see.' His expression lightened. 'Is that all? Well, you must do as you think, of course. I told Cissie to run things the way Lydia liked them, that's all. I thought it might help Alex if there was not too much change. But you have *carte blanche*, I've told you, as far as that sort of thing is concerned.'

Laura stared at him, mesmerised. It was only the second time she had heard him use Lydia's name.

'What ... what was she like?' she asked, before she could stop herself. 'Was Alex very devoted to her?' she blurted out, aware even as she spoke that it was not quite what she wanted to ask.

Robert had lit a long narrow black cigar, and he exhaled the smoke contemplatively, with an infuriating slowness, before he answered.

'I really don't know,' he said slowly, his eyes meeting hers. 'I should imagine so, wouldn't you?'

'And his father?' She was not going to be put off, she thought, taking another sip of her wine to give her courage. 'What was he like?'

'John? He was very like me.' Seeing her expression, but not, she fervently hoped, understanding it, he corrected himself. 'He *looked* like me. We were not alike in other respects.'

'Oh.' She stared at him silently, and he stood up, stretching lazily. Then with a swiftness that took her by surprise he crossed to her and took her by the arm, drawing her to her feet.

'Come on,' he said abruptly. 'I don't feel like talking. I feel like going for a drive.'

'But ...'

'I told you before, woman, no buts and no blushes. I've given up on the blushes. Not the other.'

Before she could argue or draw back, he had propelled her firmly outside and into the car. After the warmth of the house

the air was startlingly cold against her skin and her face. She
leaned back against the seat as he let in the clutch, feeling
suddenly a little lightheaded. The bourbon, she thought, and he
was right. She had never been drunk in her life, and if this was
what it felt like, it was quite fun. She heard herself laugh softly:

'Where are we going?'

'We'll know when we get there.' Robert shot her a dark
sideways glance, and she felt her heart swoop and lift.

'I shouldn't be doing this.'

'Maybe not. But tonight doesn't count. Tonight is a special
night.' He accelerated fast out of the drive and on to the
desert road. 'Tonight—just for once—*we* make the rules.'

He had switched the headlamps to full beam; the car surged
forward as he jammed his foot down on the accelerator.
Laura wound down the window so the wind that ripped over
the car caught her hair. As it blew back from her face he
glanced at her.

'You like driving fast?'

'Tonight I do.'

She could see the speedometer rising: ninety, a hundred, a
hundred and ten. The road was straight; it was wonderful, she
thought. The danger was wonderful. He was dangerous, and
he was wonderful too ... The wind whipped her hair, her
mind whirled.

Darkness sped by the car like the brush of a wing; her mind
seemed to sing with their speed. She sighed, and he gave her
an amused glance.

'Laura, I think you've been drinking.'

'So I have. So have you.'

'Yes, but I'm not drunk.'

'Neither am I!' she cried indignantly. 'Not in the least. I just
feel ...'

'What do you feel?'

'I feel free.'

'Funny,' he said, 'so do I.' And he reached across to hold
her hand, his tightening over hers as it lay in her lap; her
blood sang with happiness.

'I wish ...' she began.

'What do you wish?'

'I wish you'd drive on for ever.'

Robert laughed and instantly she felt the car slow,
decelerate, stop. He switched off the engine and the silence of
the desert was loud in her ears.

'How cruel of you!'

'Not at all.' He got out and opened her door, and then suddenly she was standing beside him in the darkness, with the sky a great arc of stars above their heads. He tilted her face deliberately up to him, and looked down into her eyes. 'Now listen to me, Laura. Are you drunk? Have you had too much to drink?'

She stared at him, feeling her mind slow, and calm itself into a suddenly alert rationality. 'No,' she said, and knew it was true.

'Good,' he said. 'Then come with me.'

Taking her hand, he led her away from the road, over rough, uneven ground that made her stumble and hold on to him. Scrub and little thorny bushes caught at her ankles. When they could no longer see the road, or the car, he stopped.

'Where are we?' She looked up into his face, shadowed in the starlight.

'In the middle of nowhere.' He took her by the shoulders and turned her, so she could see in each direction. 'You see? No lights. No towns. No houses. No people. The nearest thing to nowhere.'

'And why are we here?' she asked, as he turned her back to face him, although suddenly in her heart she knew the answer.

'So that I can kiss you,' he said, although he did not do so.

Her heart seemed to her to stop beating; the world slowed, and the moment, the silence, seemed to expand, to grow, to go on for ever. She wanted this, suddenly she knew it. At the same time, as if she had dreamed the moment before it came, she also knew what he would say next.

He took her hand and lifted it gently, so their palms rested against one another, and he looked directly into her eyes.

'I told you, tonight is different. Tonight we make the rules. We're out of time and ...' he gestured around them, 'out of place. We forget about everything else. Who I am, who you are ...' He paused. 'We forget the past.'

'And tomorrow?' she asked quietly, knowing what he would answer.

'We don't have a tomorrow, Laura, not you and I.'

His voice was gentle, and she bowed her head; she had no need to ask him why. Lydia, said a voice in her mind, and the breeze brushed her skin. He tilted her face up to him, and she looked into those dark fathomless eyes.

'So,' he said. 'On that condition, just tonight, may I break my promise?'

'Do you want to?' she asked, marvelling that her voice could sound so calm when her blood hammered in her ears and her hand trembled against his.

'God damn it, Laura,' he muttered, his voice suddenly roughened, and he pulled her into his arms. 'Why do you ask questions when you know the answers?'

She lifted her face, parted her lips. It was the last action she was conscious of making. Then his mouth came down on hers, fiercely, demandingly, and she arched her body against him. He did not speak, though once he groaned, seeking the soft skin of her throat with his lips, finding the pulse beneath the skin, as the breeze caught her hair, laying it across his, both so black in the starlight. She trembled, feeling his kisses, edged with an urgency and desperation, soar through her blood, feeling the harsh unfamiliar lines of a man's body against the softness of her own. Her arms reached up to him, encircling him, touching the skin of his face, running her fingers through the short hair at the base of his neck.

'Oh!' she cried out, a little inarticulate cry, as for a second he drew back from her mouth, and, his eyes never leaving hers, as if he had to see, measure the force of her response to him, he slowly moved his caressing hands up, from her narrow waist, so delicate that his fingers could span it, to the fullness of her breasts. She moaned, closing her eyes, as he cupped their weight in his palms, moving his fingers very delicately, slowly, so they stroked her hardening nipples.

'You want me, Laura,' he said, as if her response surprised him, as if he had doubted it. 'My sweet Laura.'

Very gently he parted the fastening of her dress, lowering his head to her breasts, touching her, there, with his tongue, so an exquisite pleasure, so sharp it was like pain, soared through her blood, and she cradled his head against her with a cry.

His breath was coming raggedly, unevenly, now, and she knew he held himself back with difficulty. All she knew, with a force of feeling that terrified her, was that she did not want him to hold back at all. But even as she knew that, she heard him sigh. Very gently, stroking her skin so it felt like silk under his touch, he withdrew his hands and fastened her dress. He kissed her lips again then, more gently this time. Then, quietly, he held her in his arms.

'No,' he said inexorably, as she tried to touch him. He drew back a little. 'I know my reputation isn't too good,' he said, 'but I do have a conscience. So don't tempt me any more, Laura. We'll only regret it.'

'I shan't regret it,' she said fiercely.

'Oh, but you would. You might not think so now, but you would.' He put his arm gently around her. 'Listen to me, Laura. Some day, probably quite soon, you'll meet someone you love, and whom you want to marry. You might regret it then. You'd probably regret it even sooner. Believe me, it's true.'

She stared at him, resentful tears starting to her eyes. 'I thought you said I ought to take a few risks in my life?'

Robert laughed softly, and touched her cheek. 'Not that one. Not with me.'

'Don't talk like that! You speak as if I were a child!'

'Do I? I didn't mean to. I don't think of you in that way at all.'

'Then how do you think of me?' She stared at him, and the silence lengthened. At last he bowed his head, and kissed her forehead gently.

'I think you ask too many questions,' he said lightly. 'And if you ask any more I shall know I've acted wrongly. Now, let me drive you home.'

He took her hand, and in silence she followed him back to the car. Neither of them spoke until they reached the house. When he had switched off the ignition they sat side by side in silence for a moment, the air electric with the tension between them. Finally he turned to her, and with a twist of compassion, she saw his face shadowed and suddenly tired.

'Laura,' he said, his voice sounding strained and formal, 'this sounds ridiculous, but I want to be sure you understand. I like you, and I admire you, and tonight—well, you look quite beautiful.' He paused, not looking at her, speaking deliberately. 'As beautiful as anything I've ever seen. And tomorrow . . .'

And tomorrow? Her heart gave a wild lurch of hope before the expression in his eyes killed it dead.

'And tomorrow you are going to go back to looking after Alex and I am going back to finish this damned film, and that must be the end of it. Do you understand?'

She stared at him, her eyes wide, pain like a knife in her heart. *Why?* she wanted to cry out, but the look in his eyes stopped the word in her throat. She fought back the tears, but she knew they shone in her eyes. She saw him set his mouth.

'Look,' he turned to her, as if willing himself to be brutal. 'You're twenty-two; I'm thirty-three. You're Alex's nurse. It would be shabby, don't you think, if we had an affair?'

She looked away, twisting her palms in her lap. 'Yes,' she said dully, 'I suppose it would.'

'So?' He looked at her tiredly.

'So, no regrets.' She forced her voice to sound light, and reached for the door handle, wondering if he knew that she felt like a swimmer miles from the shore and hopelessly out of her depth. At the last moment, when he had not stopped her, she turned back impulsively.

'But I shan't forget,' she said fiercely. 'Not with whisky, or wine, or music or driving fast or . . . any of the other things you mentioned. I shan't forget!'

She saw his face contract as if with pain, but the expression was fleeting, gone in an instant.

'Yes, you will, Laura,' he said. 'And so shall I. Now goodnight.'

She slammed the door when he said it, and raced upstairs to her room. When the door was closed and locked behind her, she bent and twisted the red shoes off her feet. Then she threw them across the room. A shabby affair; a one-night stand . . .

'I hate you, Lydia,' she said out loud.

And perhaps because she said that, in that way, she dreamed of Lydia when she finally slept that night. She had beautiful eyes, like a cat, and exquisitely manicured finger nails, brilliantly lacquered: like long red claws.

CHAPTER SEVEN

'WOULD you like to come out to the location today? You and Alex?'

Laura had been sitting alone in the kitchen, sipping coffee, her thoughts miles away. The sound of Robert's voice—she had not heard him come in—and the casual touch of his hand against her shoulder startled her. She swung round, hoping nothing on her face betrayed the fact she had been thinking of him.

'I'm sorry—I startled you.' He had drawn back, was watching her with an expression on his face she could not quite fathom. They looked at each other for a moment, without speaking. It was four days now since he had driven her out into the desert, and during that time she had seen little of him, except in the evenings. His manner then had been careful: concerned, he asked always about Alex, and listened gravely to her answers. He treated her politely but distantly; courteously but distractedly, as if his mind were elsewhere. He had never referred once to what had happened that first night, and she had not dared to. It was as if it had never happened: so much so that Laura felt as if she had dreamed it. Why did you kiss me? she had wanted to ask, so many times, but always she had managed to repress the question. The answer was obvious enough, she had told herself drily, even to someone as inexperienced as herself. Lydia had been dead almost a year: Robert Wentworth, no matter how much he might have loved her, was—as Zara had said—a man, like other men, Presumably his life was not entirely celibate. So, on an impulse, simply because she had been there . . .

'I thought Alex might enjoy it.' He hesitated, turning his eyes away from her face as if with difficulty. 'The cameras and so on.'

'I'm sure he would. He loves technical things . . . machines . . .' Her voice trailed away. Suddenly the atmosphere in the room was intensely awkward, with an undercurrent of tension beneath the banalities of their words. Robert turned back to her abruptly.

'I'm sorry,' he said. 'Kitzbuhl's been working us so hard, I've hardly seen you. And Alex.' He paused. 'I hope everything's going well? No problems? You're quite happy?'

'Oh yes, quite,' she said nervously. 'We're fine. I think Alex . . .'

She had no chance to finish what she was saying, because Cissie bustled into the room. She flung back the kitchen door, grinning at Laura, obviously not seeing Robert, who stood just behind it.

'Laura honey, Dr Graham's here. He's up with Alex now— just doin' the routine checks. You want to go and see him? He asked me to find you . . .' She gave Laura a broad wink, and Robert stepped forward quickly.

'That's all right, Cissie. There's no need to bother Laura. I'll see Graham, I want a word with him anyhow . . .'

'Oh.' Cissie registered his presence. 'But Dr Graham, he said . . .'

'Never mind what he said. I'll deal with it.' His voice was cold, curt. He swung out of the room without a backward glance. 'Laura,' he called from the hall, 'I'll send Winston to pick you and Alex up. We break at noon. Please don't be late.'

The kitchen door swung shut on his voice, and Cissie raised her eyebrows; she looked at Laura searchingly.

'What's eatin' *him*, I wonder? You bin here five days now, and you ain't seen the doctor once, 'cept that first day. Yet he keeps callin. in. I figure you ought to talk to him, you bein' Alex's nanny and all.'

Laura sighed. 'Oh, I don't know,' she said resignedly. 'I really don't need to see him anyway. There's been no change.'

'No change?' Cissie put her hands on her hips and regarded her belligerently. 'There's bin a lot of changes, I'd say. Why, Master Alex, he looks a different child now from what he did. His appetite's come back, he's runnin' around now, swimmin', playin'. Why, he looks just fine. Oh no . . .' she paused, glancing towards the door from which Robert Wentworth had exited so abruptly, 'I see plenty of changes, honey. Plenty!'

Laura looked at her, for she spoke with emphasis, but clearly Cissie decided to say no more. Instead she drew out a chair and sat down opposite Laura.

'So,' she said, 'you tell me, honey. You happy here?'

'Oh yes, of course,' Laura said quickly. 'It's so beautiful, and I enjoy being with Alex, and . . .'

'You don't feel lonesome, nothin' like that?' Cissie looked at her keenly. 'You're a long way from home, and you can't be thinkin' of a little boy, even Alex, all the time.' She hesitated. 'You got anyone special back home? A boy-friend, someone you're missin'?'

Laura smiled and shook her head. 'No, nothing like that. Why do you ask?'

'Oh, I don't know, honey. I just watched you once or twice, when you didn't know I was lookin', and I thought you looked kind of sad. Like you was missin' someone.'

'No. No, not at all,' Laura said hastily.

'I see.' Cissie did not drop her gaze. Gradually a broad grin spread across her features. 'Well, that's good,' she said at last. 'And you're goin' out to the location today, huh?' She paused.

'That's a real honour, you know that, honey? Mr Wentworth, he don't like folks watchin' when he's out workin'. Why, when his brother and his wife was out here, he wouldn't let them near the place. I heard her askin', and he said no, straight out.'

Laura stared at her. Slowly she put down her cup.

'Cissie . . .' she began.

'Yes, honey?'

'What were they like? Alex's parents?'

'Like, honey?' Cissie's face grew serious. 'Why, they were fine, just fine. Mr Wentworth now, he was a good man. Quiet, I guess, didn't say much. But deep. Like his brother.'

'And . . . Mrs Wentworth?' Laura heard her own voice tremble a little as she spoke. Cissie's face immediately took on a closed expression.

'Mrs Wentworth? Why, she was just about the most beautiful thing I've ever seen . . .' she began, then glanced at Laura. 'I think she was kind of lonely out here, you know? Most days, she just sat indoors. She hated the sun, you see, said it brought on her headaches. She just used to sit in there in the lounge, with the blinds down, playin' with those cards of hers. Settin' them out, shufflin' them, settin' them out again . . .' She sighed, and slowly levered herself up from the chair. 'Funny cards, too, with pictures on them. Couldn't play no proper games with them.'

'Tarot cards?' Laura stared at her.

'I don't know, honey. They're still there if you want to look at them. But don't let Mr Wentworth see you doin' it. He didn't hold with all that—cards, fortune-tellin'. I heard him tell her.'

Cissie turned away, obviously anxious to bring the conversation to an end, and reluctantly Laura stood up.

'You go off now, honey, and find Alex.' Cissie gave her a warm smile. 'And don't you go frettin' none about the past. You're too young. It's sad, what happened, but it's done.' She paused. 'You got to think about the future now. You and Mr Wentworth. And Alex.'

But it wasn't as easy as that, Laura thought, as the kitchen door closed behind her, and she stood in the cool of the hall. No matter how she disengaged, tried to concentrate just on Alex, thoughts of Lydia would swim back into her mind. What kind of a woman was it, she thought, that Robert

Wentworth had loved so passionately that even now, a year
after her death, he found it hard to speak her name?

On impulse—glancing up at the stairs and seeing no one
coming—she turned into the small room Cissie called the
lounge. It was at the back of the house. They never used it;
she had been in there only once before. Quickly, feeling
furtive and guilty, she shut the door behind her and stood
looking at the room. The blinds were down; the air-
conditioning whispered drily. The room was tidy, dusted, still.
Laura drew in her breath and moved forward.

The room was no different from the others in this rented
house; it was pretty, comfortable, slightly anonymous. There
was a sofa, chairs, a desk, a small card table—a card table!
Suddenly compelled, she stepped forward. Yes, Cissie was right,
they were still there, put away neatly in their pack. She hesitated,
then bent forward and picked it up. The surface of the box was
filmed with dust, the red and gold and blue of its wrappings
faded. Her hands shaking a little, she opened the pack and
spread the cards out on the table before her. She had seen Tarot
cards before, but she had no idea how to read them. Even so the
images that fanned out before her fingers were startling:
butterfly colours; a dark tower; a capering skeleton; a girl and a
man—*Les Amoureux, La Mort, La Tour Abolie.*

Two of the cards were much worn, as if they had been
handled more than the others: *Les Amoureux*; *La Mort*. Laura
stared at them quietly. Had Lydia known she was going to
die? Was that what the cards had told her?

She shivered, and then hastily, suddenly half afraid—of
what? she asked herself, of nothing, of imaginings and
shadows—she pushed the cards back into their box. The cards
carried a scent, as if from much handling, she could smell it
now, it seemed to hang on her own hands. A sweet fragrance,
slightly sickly, like tuberoses. Nervously she turned away
from the table, peering at the shadowy room, feeling
suddenly, irrationally, that she was not alone.

'Lydia?' she said uncertainly.

The room was silent. A blind at the window flapped, then
settled. Quickly she moved to the door, listening to make sure
the hall was empty, then let herself out.

On the stairs, as she went up for Alex, she met Robert
hurrying to leave for the set. Feeling guilty, ashamed now of
her imaginings, she would have passed him without a word,
but he stopped her, catching her arm.

'Laura? I'm sorry, I was rude earlier—I didn't mean to be.
I . . .' As he spoke he had teasingly raised her hand to his lips,
and before she could stop herself she had snatched it away.
Nervously she rubbed her palm against her skirt: the scent on
her fingers seemed to her now very strong; it seemed to hang
in the air between them. At once he broke off, and she saw
him tense, then frown, his eyes looking hurt and puzzled. Her
cheeks flamed instantly with colour. There was the minutest of
hesitations, then he brushed past her.

'So—are you coming out to the location, then?'

Guilt and embarrassment made her hesitate, and he gave a
gesture of impatience.

'Well, maybe we should forget it—you don't seem very
keen.'

'No, it's not that, I . . .'

'Let's leave it, then,' he cut her off brusquely. 'We're doing
the love scenes today anyway, so it's not very suitable for
Alex. And no doubt you've got better things to do than watch
a bunch of actors making a bad film. Forget I mentioned it,
O.K.?'

With that he was gone, not even glancing back over his
shoulder. Laura watched him go, disappointment acute in her.
At least Alex didn't know of the proposed trip, that was
something, but she felt terribly let down; the day stretched
before her, suddenly dull, without interest. Slowly she went
upstairs to find Alex, but before she joined him she washed
her hands, rinsing them a long time in the ice-cold water. It
was true what Zara had told her; now the last lingering doubt
had gone. She had seen it in his face, she thought, in that tiny
moment when he took her hand, scented with a dead woman's
perfume. He had loved Lydia: she haunted him still.

For almost a week after that, as the pace of filming
accelerated, she hardly saw him. She was glad, she told
herself, glad. However much she fought it, she knew his
presence disturbed her, awoke in her a terrible aching
desperation, as if she had reached some crossroad in her life,
and he was the only guide to the path she should take. In his
company she had always a sense of expectation and
frustration. Partly it was that, still, she wanted to touch him,
as if physical closeness alone could ease the ache in her heart.
But more than that she wanted to talk to him; always she had
the sense that there were a thousand things of the utmost

importance and urgency that she had to convey to him, and yet when she asked herself what they were, tried to articulate them, they slipped away from her mind into confusion. Most of all she was conscious, all the time, of regret. Not regret for anything past, but a sharper, odder emotion, as if you could regret the future. She felt as if she had glimpsed something she could not name: an indescribable content. Its prospect had been there, just for a second. Now it was gone. Time began to obsess her: she was conscious of the passing of each second, each minute, each hour when he was absent.

Her one joy, her consolation, was Alex. The quiet routine of his life, which dominated hers, was the one thing that soothed her. She let the patterns of his day dictate hers, rising early, retiring early, often before Robert returned from location. By the middle of the second week she felt calmer and stronger. A well ordered routine, she thought once, wryly, remembering what Robert had said to her. But it did work for the child, and to her surprise, it gradually worked for her too.

It helped too that Alex grew daily more relaxed, more confident, that he now looked so much fitter than he had when she arrived from England. His skin was now tanned from the sun; his limbs had rounded and filled out; the shadows under the eyes had gone; how quickly a child's body could mend, she thought. And then, always, she wondered: how long did a heart take to mend?

One evening, when she and Alex had spent a long, peaceful and contented day together, she was reading to him, sitting out on the terrace. It was a book about Red Indians, sent up the previous day from Albuquerque, where Robert ordered the toys she thought might interest the little boy.

As she came to the bottom of a page a small hand reached across and turned it. Laura heard her own voice falter, hesitate, and then go on as if nothing had happened. At the bottom of the next page the same thing happened, and again, until she reached the end of the story. Very quietly she put it down and met Alex's eyes; in his was a dart of mischief and amusement.

'Do you know this book, Alex? Has someone read it to you before?'

He shook his head, his eyes dancing.

'I *see*.' She took his hand, wondering whether to press the point or make light of it, then decided to risk it. 'You've been holding out on me, haven't you?' she said gently. 'You can read, can't you, Alex?'

A quick grin, a slight inclination of the head.

'You old faker!' She laughed softly and rumpled his hair. 'All those stories I've been reading you, and all the while . . .' She paused, an idea coming to her. 'Well, now I can send you messages, can't I, Alex? Would you like that? I tell you what, I'll write you one tonight, a secret one, and leave it under your pillow, O.K.?'

His eyes lit up at once, and that night, when he was asleep, she carefully wrote out a message in big printed characters: *Hello, Alex. Come and wake me up. Love from Laura.* Then she tucked it under his pillow.

He woke her at six-thirty; she heard the door open, the pad of bare feet across her floor; a small hand shook her arm impatiently. Instantly wide awake, she sat up; a piece of paper was thrust under her eyes. It was a painting, done with his new paints: big green trees, with oranges as large as footballs; flowers of scarlet and yellow and blue; a huge sun, bristling with rays of light, and underneath its beams two people who could only be Alex and herself, holding hands in the midst of the garden. Written in large uneven characters at the bottom it said: *God morning Laura*, followed by a spatter of crosses.

'Alex darling! It's beautiful! You understood my message—and you can write! It's us, isn't it—in the garden?'

He nodded shyly, and Laura's heart lifted with a surge of happiness. It *was* lovely, she thought, especially the mispelling. The garden in the picture looked like paradise. It was so vibrant with life, the sun was so full that it indeed looked like God's morning. She smiled at him.

'And look at all those kisses! Ten, eleven—why, that's one for every day I've been here. Right, young man, may I have them now? I claim them.'

She leaned forward, and very solemnly Alex placed eleven firm kisses on her cheek, as Laura counted them aloud.

'Well,' she said, slipping out of bed to join him, 'now we can have a regular old correspondence, you and I. I shan't have to play guessing games any more, shall I? I know . . .' Hastily she found another piece of paper and a pencil. 'While I get dressed, why don't you write me a list of all the things you'd like for breakfast? Then we'll go and get them, all right?'

When she came back, Alex was kneeling on the floor, his

tongue between his teeth, concentration manifest in every line
of his body. He handed her the piece of paper proudly. It said:

Wofels

Sirop

Milc

Laura clapped her hands delightedly. 'Right,' she said, 'I
know exactly what to get now. Come on, Alex!'

Downstairs the kitchen was cool and empty; there was no
sign of Cissie. Companionably they made the breakfast, then
carried it out to the terrace, which was just beginning to grow
warm in the slanting golden light of early morning. The air
was still; the scent of the constantly watered earth rose up
sweetly; below them birds she could not identify darted
between the trees. God's morning: Laura felt joy rise in her
unchecked; for the first time since she had come here, she
realised, her happiness felt unclouded.

Alex had some muesli, some yoghurt and fruit, three
waffles and two glasses of milk. While Laura finished her
toast he moved away a little, playing at making shadow
pictures on the tiles of the terrace.

Laura watched him contentedly, plans starting to form in
her mind. She must tell Tony Graham about this, she
thought. Robert too, of course, but she had no idea when she
might get a chance to talk to him. But Alex was going into the
nearest town, Taos, for more tests this morning; Dr Graham
would be there. She could go with him, Winston would take
them. And perhaps, after the visit to the hospital, they could
make a little trip somewhere. Robert had said they might, if
they chose. And there was a small Navajo reservation not far
from Taos that Cissie had mentioned. Alex was obsessed with
Indians, fascinated by them, by tales of tepees and tracking
and bows and arrows. He would like it; it would make a
change. Why, since she had come here they had hardly left the
confines of the house and garden . . .

As she watched him, her mind suddenly active with plans, a
shadow fell across her arm. She started, turning, shielding
her eyes from the sun, to see Robert Wentworth; he had come out
on to the terrace quite silently, and was standing watching
them both.

'Oh . . .' She stood up quickly, nervously smoothing the
creases from her skirt. 'I didn't think . . . I thought you'd have
left for location.'

He smiled at her easily. 'I've a later call today, thank God.

We're ahead of schedule. Kitzbuhl thinks we might finish early. Not that it's surprising, the way he's been driving us the last few days.' He hesitated, and then held out his arms awkwardly to the child. 'Hi, Alex. Have you missed me? I've hardly seen anything of you both for days.'

There was a second's pause, then the little boy nodded energetically. Suddenly he launched himself into the man's arms, and with a shout of laughter Robert lifted him high in the air and held him there.

'You're looking terrific, Alex, you know that? I reckon you've grown at least an inch this past week. And look at those muscles! Here, let me feel . . .'

Gently he lowered the boy to the ground and solemnly felt his upper arms.

'Flex them a bit, you know, the way I showed you . . .'

Alex clenched his fist and bent his arm dutifully, and the man let out a long low whistle.

'Incredible! Practically heavyweight class. A few more weeks and you'll fell me with a single blow!'

Alex promptly aimed a small fist at his solar plexus, and Robert obligingly doubled up with a convincing grunt of pain. The two sparred together for a few minutes, and then, regretfully, the man looked at his watch.

'Hell!' He turned to Laura. 'I'll have to go. Kitzbuhl's idea of a late start is seven-thirty. Still . . .' he grinned at them happily, 'it would be good if we finished early, wouldn't it? Then no more appointments, just England, Marston, no work, and the best summer ever. How does that sound to you?'

'It sounds wonderful,' said Laura, and Alex nodded, looking up at the tall dark man beside him with an expression of open hero-worship.

'Right, I'll see what I can arrange.' He dropped a quick kiss on Alex's hair. 'Look after Laura for me, won't you?' Then he turned; Laura moved quickly.

'I'll see you out,' she said casually. 'You wait here, Alex. Do some more shadow pictures. I shan't be a moment.'

Alex went back happily to his game; she saw Robert's face register a second's surprise, then together they went into the house.

In the cool shadowed hall he put his arm lightly around her shoulders: in a comradely sort of way, Laura thought, flinching.

'This is a pleasant surprise . . .' He shot her the old teasing sideways glance, and Laura felt her heart jump.

'I . . . I just wanted a quick word . . .'

He stopped instantly.

'Is something wrong? You're not unhappy, are you? Is Alex all right?'

'No, no, we're both fine. I just wanted to ask you. Alex has to go into Taos today for his checks, and I wondered if I might go with him.'

'Why?' His face had gone suddenly cold; he removed the arm from her shoulders.

'I wanted to have a talk with Dr Graham, if I could,' she said hesitantly, bewildered by the change in his manner. 'You see, yesterday I found out that Alex . . .'

She never completed the sentence; he turned sharply away.

'Of course. You don't need my permission to go out, you know. You're not a prisoner. Go, by all means. Winston can take you.'

'But . . .'

'I can't stop now, I'm afraid. I'm late as it is. I may see you later.'

And with that he was gone, without a backward glance, Laura stared after him as he strode across the forecourt and into the long black car that awaited him. Disappointment welled up in her. She had so much wanted to tell him the news about Alex. He had seemed perfectly goodhumoured, elated even, out on the terrace. And now this. How moody, how unpredictable he was, she thought dully.

She turned back, then paused. When they spoke they had been standing by the door into the little shadowed room Lydia had used, where she had set out her Tarot. Was it that which had caused the change—perhaps brought back some sudden memory? Perhaps. If it was, she realised, she preferred not to know. She went back, all her optimism and elation seeping away from her, to join Alex.

In the car going to Taos she tried to concentrate on the view from the windows: it was so beautiful. The mountains in the distance, their rugged outline already shimmering indistinct in the heat, the clear curve of the road, slicing through the flatlands of the desert. The Sangre de Cristo mountains, she thought; the Navajo reservation was there. They would go there later; perhaps that would cheer her. As it was, she felt suddenly as if all the equilibrium she had carefully built up over the past days had been destroyed in an instant, with a glance, a touch, a change of manner. She sighed, and turned to Alex.

At the hospital, when Alex had trotted off quite happily for his tests—which he seemed to regard as so many games—she bumped into Tony Graham, not recognising him for an instant in his white coat. When she told him she had come in specially, that she wanted to talk to him, his face lit up in a delighted grin.

'Great,' he said. 'I come off duty at one. Have lunch with me. Alex won't be through till later.'

'Oh, I don't know.' She hesitated. 'I was going to take Alex on after, you see—to that Indian reservation, the one in the mountains. Cissie told me about it.'

'No problem.' He grinned. 'Send Winston back, and I'll take you both over. Las Cruces? That the place? I treat a couple of the kids there—I know it well. I can take you back to the house afterwards.'

'But I don't want to impose on you . . .' Laura hesitated. 'You can't have much time off and . . .'

'Quit arguing! It's fixed. Meet me at one. There's a Mexican restaurant in the main square—you can't miss it. I'll see you there.'

And before she could protest any more he had gone. Laura told Winston he needn't wait for them—and that was much better for him, she told herself defensively, wondering why she felt a little uneasy about this plan. Then she set off down the road from the hospital to the centre of the town. Light dazzled her; it was the hottest it had been since she came out from England, and the low-built white adobe houses reflected all the heat back into the dusty road. Within a hundred yards her dress was damp with sweat; her hair hung heavily like an unwelcome shawl. Impatiently she tossed it back, glad when she reached the central square of Taos, and the comparative cool of its trees and shade. She walked about for a while, curious to explore, yet feeling oddly on edge. There was a good hour to kill.

She wandered into one of the churches built by seventeenth-century Jesuit priests, a tiny white building, its walls thick mud like that of the traditional houses, topped with a mission bell. Inside it was empty, still. The harsh light was diffused by small windows and thick glass; for a while Laura sat, feeling at peace, and feeling also something else which she could not

quite define. Safe perhaps; here the memories that jangled and
alerted her nerves seemed to calm.

But after a little while she went out again and wandered
around the streets, looking in the windows of the shops. It
was a little touristy, a little garish, old and new America cheek
by jowl. But in some of the shops there were beautiful things:
exquisite Navajo jewellery, silver and turquoise. The famous
Navajo rugs, with their faded vegetable dyes, their intricate
patternings. To her their abstractions were unreadable, but
she knew that to an Indian the zig-zags and lines and crosses
carried a meaning as clear and direct as words; they could
read these shapes as a blind man might read braille. Some
signified the Navajo belief in the four layers of the world, a
man in one of the shops told her, seeing her interest, other
is their journeying, and the rituals of their gods.

'The Navajo have a matriarchal religion,' the man told her.
'Their most powerful deity is a woman.' He smiled. 'Their term
for her is kind of difficult to translate. The Spider Woman, some
call her, because she spins the web of fate. I prefer the other
translation: the Changing Woman. Less creepy, don't you think?'

'The Changing Woman?' Laura stared at him.

'Yeah. She dictates and alters men's destinies.' He grinned.
'Pretty potent stuff!'

Laura left the shop, feeling again on edge, wondering why
that scrap of information should have started the unaccount-
able nervousness that once more sharpened her senses. She
looked down at her watch. Half an hour to go. Perhaps she
could find a toy-shop, she thought, trying to be purposeful. It
would be good to buy something for Alex.

She was just turning back to the square when a building
caught her eye. *The Sante Fe and Taos Examiner*. She
hesitated and then crossed the street.

The offices were small but modern: plate glass windows,
with Venetian blinds, and beyond them a reception area with
tables and newspapers. One wall was covered with news
photographs in black and white. Laura stared in through the
windows. Across the street a canopy flapped once, twice, in a
sudden dry gust of breeze. A child kicked a can; it clattered
along the sidewalk. Laura shivered, braced herself, and
pushed open the door.

'Good morning . . .' she stared hesitantly at the young man
behind the reception desk. From rooms behind him came the
clatter of typewriters, the chatter of a Telex machine.

'Hi. What can I do for you?' He was about nineteen, freckled. His eyes travelled briefly over her figure, and apparently approved of what he saw.

Her voice felt suddenly dry in her throat. 'Is it possible to look at back numbers of your newspaper?'

'Depends how far back you want to go. Before 1950 it's in the basement, and we've got problems.'

'No, not so far back.' She attempted a stiff smile. 'Quite recently. Spring last year.'

'That's O.K. Nothin' easier. Know what dates?'

She lowered her eyes. She did know. Cissie had told her, in passing one day. She had not forgotten.

'It would be March—the fifteenth. Maybe if I could look at the sixteenth too . . .'

'Sure.' He gestured to one of the chairs. 'Take a seat. You're English, right? It'll take me a coupla seconds to locate it.'

Her hands were shaking; they were damp with sweat. She sat down at the table, her back rigid, fighting the impulse to get up there and then and leave, before he came back. But she didn't move; she couldn't move. *I have to know*, she thought; *I have to know*. The phrase repeated itself insanely in her mind, like a stupid refrain of music she could not dislodge.

'Here—the fifteenth and the sixteenth. How's that?' He was looking at her curiously as he slid the papers across the table towards her. 'You lookin' for any particular thing? Want me to check anything out for you?'

'No. Yes,' she corrected herself as she saw a flicker of doubt cross his face. 'The—er—real estate section.'

His face cleared. 'You'll find it at the back.'

'Thank you.'

'You're welcome.'

He turned away; Laura did not even look up. It was there, on the front page under a banner headline: *Movie star's brother dies in crash*. The black letters were an inch high; they danced on the page before her. She hadn't expected this; foolishly, forgetting Robert's fame, she had expected to find a small item, maybe just a few column inches. But this . . .

The words of the report made no sense to her; she could not read them. It was the photograph that held her eyes, huge, slightly blurred, taking up half the page . . . She stared at it in horror. The car was almost unrecognisable as a car. Buckled under what must have been its bonnet and crushing down on

what remained of its roof was a telegraph pole, its wires
trailing across the wreckage. Under it lay a mass of twisted
warped metal. The front of the car was contorted into a
jagged bunch of steel; the windscreen had been obliterated.
What remained of the door on the driver's side hung open on
its hinges; just below it, in a mess of seeping oil and shattered
glass, lay what was just recognisable as a woman's high-heeled
sandal.

Nausea rose in her throat; her hands shook. So that was
how Lydia had died! She thought, dear God, how *fast* were
they going? And instantly the memory came back to her: oh
yes, they can all make one forget: whisky, bourbon, *driving
too fast*. And in the second the memory came to her she
realised something else, something which had simply never
occurred to her. Lydia had been driving.

CHAPTER EIGHT

SHE stared down at the words of the report, its phrases
becoming disjointed before her eyes. *At 3 p.m., on Route 88
. . . John and Lydia Wentworth . . . brother to . . . fire service
and medical teams . . . oxyacetylene cutting equipment . . . three
hours . . . wreckage scattered over a wide area.* Suddenly the
sentences took shape; Laura felt her blood go cold. The
deceased woman's red sandal, and her wedding ring, were
found a few feet from the wreck . . .

Red sandals. Her wedding ring. Laura stared at the picture
stupidly. Could you lose your wedding ring in a crash like
that?

Her mind feeling frozen, she read on. There were a few
terse comments from the local police chief. Yes, the crash
had obviously happened at high speed. No, there was no
obvious cause; visibility was perfect; the road was straight.
Possibly there had been a tyre blow-out. Lydia Wentworth
had been driving, and she was a teetotaller, so intoxication
could be ruled out. Yes, death must have been in-
stantaneous: the steering wheel pin had passed right through
the . . .

Heart, Laura thought, pushing the paper away. She could
not bear to read any more. Horror and pity welled up inside

her, and a sick anger with herself that she should have acted as she had.

As she pushed the paper away, the front page of the other edition the boy had brought her was suddenly visible. In spite of her feelings it compelled her eyes. There, almost full-page, were two photographs; one was Lydia, the other Robert Wentworth. She stared at them stupidly, feeling her skin grow chill. Then, as the words of the captions penetrated her mind, she realised her mistake. It was Lydia all right; there was no mistaking that pale oval face, the helmet of gold hair. But the other photograph was not of Robert Wentworth; it was his brother. And, as he had said, the likeness was extraordinary. They might almost have been twins. Only with careful scrutiny was the difference between them apparent. His brother's face was slightly heavier, thicker around the jawline; and the eyes, they were different too. There was an openness in their regard; his was a kind face, without danger, without that suggestion of mockery, of self-distancing that was so marked in the actor's face.

Abruptly, feeling sick, Laura stood up. She gathered up the papers, her hands dirty with their ink, and handed them back to the boy behind the desk. It was obvious they had not been opened, that the real estate section at the back had not been consulted, and she saw the curiosity in his face, but was beyond caring.

'You found what you were lookin' for, miss?'

Laura did not answer. She pushed the paper at him and, turning, hurried from the place. He called something after her, but she did not pause. Outside in the street, hastening back to the square, she looked nervously over her shoulder. Suddenly, irrationally, she felt as if she were being followed. But the street was empty in the heat; the canvas awning flapped as before; above the road the air shimmered. In the far distance, miles away down the straight road that must lead out of town, she could just see the black shape of a car, travelling fast, its wheels throwing up dust, coming that way. She looked at it, for no reason afraid, and then broke into a run.

'Hey, you look as white as a sheet! You seen a ghost or something?' Tony Graham stood up as she came into the small dark Mexican restaurant and reached for her hand. 'What's wrong? Is it the heat?'

She shook her head, and sank gratefully into the small wooden chair opposite him.

'No, it's nothing. I'm fine. I'm just hungry, I think.'

The clear blue eyes scanned her face briefly, but he made no comment. He turned to the waitress.

'Two margaritas.'

The drinks arrived in two shallow glasses, their edges rimmed with salt. Laura's hand shook as she raised the glass to her lips; the tequila was mixed with something sweet; sugar and salt on the tongue. The words on the menu blurred before her eyes, and without speaking, Tony Graham took the slightly greasy red folder from her hands, and turned back to the waitress.

'We'll just have tacos,' he said. 'And then chili.'

When the woman had gone there was a brief silence. Above their heads a ceiling fan rotated, its propellers stirring the warm air, shifting it, but not cooling it. Tony Graham sat upright, his two large square hands resting on the table between them. The silence lengthened.

'O.K.,' he said at last. 'Something's wrong. What?'

Laura met his eyes. 'I went to the newspaper offices,' she told him. 'I looked at the back numbers. I saw the photographs—of the crash.'

'I see.' He looked down at the table, shifted his knife a few centimetres. 'And why did you do that?'

'I don't know. I hadn't planned to. I just saw the place, and suddenly . . .'

'You thought it might explain something?'

'Yes. No—I don't know. It wasn't like that. I wasn't thinking it out. I just . . .' She broke off.

'I think you do know, Laura. Why you did that.' Tony was looking at her steadily. Abruptly she drained her glass and put it down on the table.

'Yes,' she said, 'you're right. I do. I . . . wanted to know how it happened, I suppose, but it wasn't really that. I wanted to know about Lydia.'

There was a moment's silence, then he smiled. 'Well,' he said gently, 'we're getting someplace. I reckon that's truthful at least.'

Laura leaned across the table eagerly, without shame.

'Tell me,' she said. 'You met her. No one will talk about her. Please, if you would just tell me—what was she like?'

The shrewd blue eyes met hers, then he looked away again. He moved the fork a few centimetres so it lined up with the knife, and when he spoke again he did not look up.

'She was very beautiful,' he said flatly. 'But you know that.' He paused. 'She had . . . an extraordinary effect on men. I've never seen anything quite like it.' He smiled, his voice dry. 'I wouldn't say even I was totally immune to it.'

'But you didn't like her?'

'No. You're very quick—I didn't. But in her case, liking hadn't got a whole lot to do with it.'

'You mean she was attractive.' She drew in her breath. 'Sexually attractive.'

Tony repressed a grin, and Laura felt her temper quicken.

'Don't tease me,' she said hotly. 'Don't mock. I'm not a child. I know perfectly well what you mean.'

'O.K.' His face grew serious, and she saw him hesitate. 'I'll try and explain. She wasn't obvious, you know what I mean? She was very English. A bit haughty, cold. I don't know . . .' He ran his fingers through his hair. 'Also nervous—nervy. She was odd. It was like she was looking for something all the time—some answer. And she thought you might have it.'

There was a silence, while the waitress brought two plates of tacos and placed them before them, during which Tony Graham's clever blue eyes never left her face. Eventually he picked up his napkin with an impatient gesture.

'Look,' he said, 'let's quit beating about the bush. You think all this relates to Alex's problem in some way, don't you? Is that why you're playing the sleuth?'

Laura blushed. 'I suppose it must be.'

'Well, I think you're right, and I think you're going to end up where I did—no place, chasing your own tail. There's only two people could tell you the truth about what went on in that family. One can't speak, and the other won't. Give up on it, Laura. I did, months ago.'

'Two people?' She looked at him curiously.

'Sure. Alex and Robert. So forget it.'

'But what if it's important?'

'Too bad.' He shrugged. 'Look, for what it's worth, I'll tell you what I thought, off the record. I thought that marriage was a hollow sham. I thought John Wentworth was one of the saddest men I've ever met. And I thought Lydia was on auto-destruct. I figured on an O.D. with painkillers, though, not an automobile accident.'

'What?'

He looked away uncomfortably, as if suddenly aware he had said too much.

'She was on high-strength medication—acute migraine. It got worse after she came out here. One of my colleagues was treating her—that's how I met them.'

Laura stared at him, her throat dry. 'You mean you think she meant to kill herself? That it wasn't an accident?'

'The thought crossed my mind.'

'But her husband ... Alex ... they were in the car with her ...'

'Yeah, they were.'

'It's not possible. No one could do that!'

'Maybe not.' Tony lowered his eyes, his face closed. Again there was a silence, and then suddenly, with a gesture of angry impatience, he slammed his palm down on the table. 'Goddammit, Laura, do you imagine I haven't tried to find out? Something happened in that car, before the crash. You read the paper. You think in a wreck like that a woman's wedding ring gets neatly torn off her finger and thrown out? No way. Something happened, something was said. Maybe there was an almighty row—who knows? It's likely enough, I'd say.'

'And Alex heard it? Is that what you mean?'

'I mean Alex is traumatised. And I don't think it's just because of the wreck, that's all. And don't ask my reasons, I don't have them. Call it instinct, if you like ...'

'I have the same instinct,' she said quietly, cutting him off.

He sighed. 'You do? Well, take my advice, and leave it alone.' He paused, then spoke more kindly. 'You're getting too involved, you know that, don't you, Laura? And I think you ought to ask yourself why. Is it because of Alex?'

'Of course it is!'

'You're sure?' The blue eyes met hers unwaveringly. 'Just Alex? Nobody else?'

'Well, naturally I'm concerned for ... for Mr Wentworth too. I mean, he's terribly worried about Alex. If I can help in any way ...'

'Sure, I get the picture.'

Something odd, and suddenly dismissive, in his voice, brought the blood to her cheeks.

'You don't believe me?'

Tony smiled, touched her hand and then quickly withdrew his own. 'Let's just say I'd like to believe it, Laura, and let's leave it at that. Right? Now, eat. And let's have a change of subject, shall we? I bring a nice English

girl out to lunch, and what happens? I find she's putting
her pretty little hand right into a nest of scorpions.
So—back off, the way I did.' He grinned at her. 'Now, try
the tacos.' His tone was final, so Laura did as she was bid.
The tacos—a kind of crisp rolled pancake—were filled with
a pungent, delicious meat sauce. She took one bite, and her
eyes instanty watered. Tony Graham let out a shout of
laughter.

'Takes the roof of your mouth off, doesn't it? And this is
nothing. You should try them south of the border!'

He had said they should change the subject, and—
obviously determined that they should—he humoured her
along until gradually she began to relax. He told her stories
about the region, about his hunting trips to the mountains,
about the winter skiing up in Colorado, where he kept a small
house.

'It's great up there,' he said warmly. 'You'd really like it,
Laura. I'd love to show you some time. Still . . .' he broke off,
'I guess you'll be going back to England soon.'

'Quite soon. Maybe the end of the week. The film's ahead
of schedule.'

'Too bad. Maybe I could swing a trip to Europe this fall.
Drop in on you, check on Alex's progress. See how you're
getting along.'

'Do you think you might?'

He smiled, his voice dry. 'I think I'd like to. But I suspect
that I am *not* going to get an invitation. Not from Robert
anyway.'

'Oh, but surely . . .'

'We'll see. I kind of doubt it. Robert's opinion of me seems
to have taken a downturn in the past two weeks. I can't think
why.'

'I don't understand . . . and I'm sure you're wrong.' Laura
stared at him in bewilderment. 'He admires you very much.
He's terribly grateful for what you've done for Alex.'

'Sure. But I know when I'm being eased out. I'm sensitive
that way.' He grinned at her. 'So, from now on, it's over to
you, Laura. And from what I saw of Alex this morning,
things can only get better. You must be pleased yourself?'

'Yes, I am,' she hesitated, still a little puzzled by his
manner. 'I discovered something about Alex yesterday. It was
why I wanted to see you. I don't know if you realised, but
Alex can read and write.'

'What?' He let out a long, low whistle. 'You really mean it? How did you find out?'

Quickly she told him, then brought out from her bag the painting Alex had given her that morning. Tony looked at it for a long while, his face gradually lighting up with delight.

'But this is fantastic! Great!' He handed it back to her. 'We tried him on all that, you know, a few months back. Word and picture correlation games—you know the kind of thing? And we got nothing—no response. We knew he hadn't started in on school, so we just assumed . . .' He grinned. 'That cunning little devil! He was holding out on us all that time. It looks like you're really getting through to him, Laura.'

'So—what do you think I should do now?'

'Keep right on the way you've been doing. I shan't interfere. In fact, I think we should drop the test sessions and the therapy. I've thought that for a few weeks. All they do is remind the kid that he's unusual in some way, sick. It would do no harm to drop them. And since you're all going back to England anyhow . . .' He stood up. 'I'll talk to Robert about it. Now, shall we go collect Alex?'

They left the restaurant and went out into the sunshine. Tony Graham's warm approval, and Alex's obvious excitement when they picked him up, helped to lift Laura's spirits for a while. She enjoyed the drive to the Navajo township, across the desert basin, and then up a winding road into the Sangre de Cristo mountains. But when they arrived at the reservation, Tony Graham—obviously a familiar visitor—was quickly drawn off by a crowd of chattering Indian children, taking Alex with him, and she was left to wander around by herself. It was a depressing place, she thought—spectacularly beautifully sited, but poverty-stricken—a street of ramshackle wooden huts and corrugated iron shanties, without trees, without shade. Chickens by the roadside; under a rusted shelter thin mules flicked their tails and twitched their hides against the swarms of flies. By the entrance to the village a pile of old pick-up trucks, their engines and wheels obviously pillaged to repair other vehicles, lay rusting in the sun. Immediately her sense of unease returned. She looked away from the heap of twisted metal, trying not to think of what she had read that morning, what had been said that lunchtime. Tony Graham was right, she thought; she was allowing herself to get too involved, too caught up in the web of the past. After all, she knew more of the circumstances than the doctor. Lydia had married the wrong man, that was all, the wrong brother. But that hadn't stopped her from . . .

She turned away. A breeze blew down the narrow pitted road; red dust smarted in her eyes, the sun burned her skin. From the far end of the village she heard the laughter of children, caught the sound of the doctor's voice, then there was silence. The street was deserted; further along a door banged, swung, banged again in the breeze. It was like a ghost town, she thought, and suddenly, unreasonably, she was afraid.

If only she could be out of this merciless sun, away from the dry wind that blew up from the desert floor. She shivered, hesitated, then crossed the street. There was a wooden shack there—it looked abandoned. But it had a dilapidated wooden verandah that afforded a tiny patch of shade. As she crossed to it she knew she was wrong; someone lived there. There was a curtain nailed across the doorway, and as she stepped forward it was drawn back; a woman looked out at her. She was Indian, very old. Her hair was white, drawn back tightly from a strong-boned, deeply lined face. Their eyes met, and the woman beckoned. Laura hesitated, uncertain, held by her narrowly spaced black eyes. She beckoned again, more forcefully, and then, as Laura moved closer, reached out a strong hand and clasped her arm. She drew her into a tiny room, shaded from the sun, close with heat. Most of its space was occupied by a huge hand loom; there were two wooden chairs.

'Water?' The woman's voice was deep, cracked. She gestured to Lara to sit down.

'Yes, I . . .' Laura hesitated awkwardly. But her throat felt tight and dry with the heat, so she did as she was bid. Instantly the woman turned away, pouring water from a pitcher into a small cracked pottery cup. She held it out with both hands.

'Drink.'

Again Laura hesitated. The shack was filthy; it smelled slightly fetid, of animals and dust; the cup was not clean. Then, not wishing to seem rude or ungrateful, she smiled and lifted the cup to her lips. The water was warm, but it eased the dryness of her throat. She drank, then handed it back, inclining her head.

'Thank you.'

The woman had sat down beside her. To her surprise, she

took the cup, placed it on the floor, but held on to Laura's hand. Her grip was astonishingly strong. Again their eyes met, and Laura felt a lurch of embarrassment and unease. The old woman was looking at her intently, with a fixity that seemed not altogether sane. She leaned forward.

'I can see,' she said.

Her voice was guttural, her accent American, with a curious hesitancy and weight as if mentally she translated each word from another language as she spoke.

'Yes?' Laura looked at her in confusion, and then to the door. Whatever had she let herself in for? Where was Tony Graham?

'Open your hand.'

Suddenly Laura understood. She looked back at the woman with a flash of comprehension. So this was some some kind of fortune-telling routine—Cissie had spoken of something of the kind, though she had said there were Indian women who could sense auras, not read palms. It was a well-known ploy for getting gullible tourists to part with their money.

'No, please.' She tried to draw her hand back. 'I don't want . . .'

'Open your hand.'

The dark eyes met hers once more, the pressure on her fingers strengthened. Laura sighed, feeling a sudden sense of pity for the woman. She had money with her, after all, and this woman clearly needed it more than she did. Why not? Slowly, compelled in spite of herself by the glittering blackness in the old woman's eyes, she uncurled her fingers.

'Ah . . .!' The woman let out a long deep sigh. She did not look down at the open palm before her, but placed her own on it, as if measuring its length against her own dry cracked skin. She lifted her other hand, very slowly, and then raised it, holding it close to Laura's face. Her face had gone blank, flat, without expression. She closed her eyes.

'Ah . . .!' She sighed again. She had begun to rock gently back and forward in the chair, and Laura repressed a smile. All part of the performance, she told herself sternly; at any moment she'd be told she was going to meet a tall dark stranger. And I've done that already, she thought.

The woman said nothing. She appeared to have gone into a trance, still rocking back and forth, her breath coming raspingly in her throat. Laura stared at her, mesmerised in spite of herself. The breathing was regular, hypnotic, it was beginning to affect her, she could sense it. It made her want to close her eyes. She felt her lids flutter, and in that second, as if flashed on her retina, she saw an image, of Robert Wentworth. It was gone in an instant; it came from nowhere. It was as if a slide had been inserted into a projector, slotted in front of the lens, then removed. She felt a stab of alarm and her eyes jerked open. The old woman was looking at her, her eyes glazed and unseeing.

'This is the man.'

She lifted her hand, moved it so it was between their faces. Fascinated, Laura stared at it, unable to look away. The patterning of the skin, the whorls and lines around the bony knuckles, seemed suddenly huge and infinitely various, a landscape, the skin of the earth seen from far away, from space perhaps ... Her own eyelids flickered again; suddenly she was conscious of nothing but compression, darkness and heat—an oppressive heat. She couldn't breathe, it was so hot. Her chest hurt; it was like breathing blood.

She opened her eyes, focusing them before her with difficulty, trying to force her mind back to rationality. If she stayed in this room any longer she would faint, she thought. Then she stared. The woman stood up, let go of her hand. She was backing away from her across the room, her arm still up in front of her face, but the gesture was different now, as if she were warding something off. Her eyes were wide, her mouth contorted, as if with fear. A stream of incomprehensible words poured from her lips.

'Please ...' Suddenly afraid, Laura stood up, and took a step towards her.

In that instant the curtain at the door was drawn back, and Tony Graham stood in the doorway.

'Laura?' He peered uncertainly into the shadows of the room, and she turned to him with swift relief. 'What's going on?' She saw him pause, look from her to the old woman, and his mouth tightened.

'I don't quite know.' She bent and picked up her bag from the floor. 'I came in for some water. And then I think I was having my fortune told, or something like that. And then ...'

Nervously she turned back to the old woman. She was shuffling about at the back of the room now, her head bowed, as if unwilling to meet their gaze.

'Damnation!' He turned to the woman, and said something in a language Laura couldn't understand, his tone sharp, inquisitive. The woman mumbled something, and Laura felt again a shaft of pity for her.

'Look, Tony, please . . .' She fumbled with her bag. 'It doesn't matter. It was interesting . . . to begin with. She just scared me a bit, that's all.'

'We'd better go.'

He held the curtain back, but Laura shook her head.

'No, wait, I ought to give her something. I'm sure that she . . .' She drew some dollars out of her purse and held them out to the old woman awkwardly, smiling.

'Please,' she said, 'take them. Thank you.'

To her surprise, the woman lifted up her arm before her face again. She shook her head vehemently. Laura looked at Tony Graham uncertainly.

'Have I done the wrong thing?'

'Not in my experience.' He looked at the woman grimly and said something again, in the language that sounded so odd, so utterly foreign.

To her dismay the woman reacted violently. Reaching across, she knocked Laura's hand away. Then she spat on the floor. Her eyes met those of the young doctor, and she said something, just a short phrase, but Laura saw his eyes widen.

'Come on.' He took her arm abruptly, and pulled her out into the sunlight. 'I shouldn't have left you alone. It's getting late and we ought to go back. Alex is waiting in the car.'

He began to propel her back down the street, hurrying so she had to run to keep up with him.

'But what was all that?' Laura plucked at his sleeve, but he didn't slacken his pace.

'A whole lot of hocus-pocus. Tricks for the tourists. They all it aura-reading. I know that woman. It's all fakery. Forget it.'

She stopped, then followed him more slowly. His back was rigid with anger.

'But why wouldn't she take my money? Surely if it's tricks for the tourists, she would. I don't understand . . .'

'God knows. Forget it. I shouldn't have brought you here.'

'Wait!' She stopped again, so he too had to pause, and when she saw his face she saw at once that it was troubled.

'She said something, didn't she? At the end—just before we left—what was it?'

'Nothing. Some trash.' He looked away. 'You don't want to believe any of that rubbish. It's nothing to do with their true beliefs, the old religion. It's just bastardised stuff, a quick way to earn a buck.' He gestured to the little group of shacks. 'Who can blame them? We ripped them off. I guess it's their turn.'

'What did she say? Why wouldn't she take my money?'

He shrugged and turned away. 'I don't know—let's get back.'

'No.' Laura held her ground, so he was forced to stop and meet her gaze. 'You do know! And I'm not getting in that car till you tell me.'

'O.K.' He glared at her. 'Have it your own way. It'll only upset you.'

'What did she *say*?'

'She said you were unlucky.' He glanced away down the empty road. 'She said . . .' He hesitated. 'She said you were close to death. Have been and will be.'

'Oh.' She stared at him blankly, unable to speak, realising only that she was not surprised.

'Laura.' He moved quickly to her and put an arm round her shoulders. 'You don't know when to leave well alone, do you? And now—you see? I knew it would get to you.'

'No, no.' She shook her head. 'It's all right, really. I'd rather know the truth.'

'Truth?' He gave a gesture of impatience. 'I told you, it's junk. You don't need an Indian seer to tell you you're close to death. A doctor will do. We all are—I could tell you that.'

She could see he was trying to cheer her up. She could also see that he was not convinced; at the back of his eyes there was a nervousness. He met her gaze with difficulty. Yet, curiously, she did not feel afraid. She felt calm, as if what the Indian woman had said merely confirmed something, something she had sensed, not just here in Navajo territory, but before. At Marston.

Tony's arm tightened around her shoulders. 'So, let's go.' He grinned at her encouragingly. 'And relax—I'll drive real slow!'

The light was beginning to fade as they reached the car. In the back seat was Alex, bubbling with excitement, clutching the spoils of his visit, a leather wristband and an eagle's feather. At the wheel Laura saw Tony hesitate for a second.

'We'll take the short route back,' he said finally. 'It's getting late. I don't want Robert worrying.'

'Fine,' said Laura, climbing into the back beside Alex.

Something in the doctor's face puzzled her. It was not until they were almost home that she realised why he looked so uneasy. Alex was so absorbed in his new belongings that whenever he looked out the window, he saw none of the road signs. But Laura did. The road they took back was not winding, like the one they had taken from Taos. It was straight as an arrow, stretching out before them across the desert floor. She knew where they were instantly, with the certainty of clairvoyance. Sure enough the signs eventually confirmed it. They were on Route 88.

CHAPTER NINE

WHEN they reached the house the sun was low in the sky. With a crunch of gravel Tony pulled the car up abruptly right behind Robert Wentworth's long black Lincoln. So he was back from filming, Laura thought nervously, and as she glanced up at the windows of the house she saw a movement, had the feeling they were watched.

'I'm coming in. I want to talk to Robert. You'd better get Alex to bed—he's had a long day.' Tony slammed his door and came round to help her out, his handsome face unsmiling and grim.

'Fine.' Laura took Alex by the hand; he was yawning widely. 'I'll get him into bed—I might have a rest myself. It was so hot today, I'm exhausted.'

Tony gave her a sharp glance.

'You're feeling all right? Not worried—I don't want you to . . .'

She shook her head, smiling. 'I'm fine. Really.'

In the hall he took her hand; at the back of the house Laura heard a door shut, footfalls.

'I may not see you again before you leave.' He hesitated. 'You said the end of the week, right? And I'm flying up to a conference in Santa Barbara tomorrow. I'll be away three days. So . . .' He paused. 'Just remember, I might fix that Europe trip—and meantime, if you need me, call. Day or night. I mean it, Laura.'

'Of course.' She pressed his hand warmly. 'Thank you for today.' She paused. 'And I'll remember your advice. I'm sure you're right.'

'Oh, and Laura . . .' She had been about to turn away, but he stayed her, reaching his hand up to his neck. Around it he was wearing the thin chain, the small medallion she had noticed the first day they met. Quickly bending his head, he slipped it off. 'For you,' he said awkwardly, holding it out to her. 'You can't leave without a souvenir.'

'For me?' Laura stared at him. The blue and silver medallion glinted in his hand.

'That's right. Here.' Before she could move he slipped it over her head, and she felt the metal cool against her skin.

'But . . .'

'No arguments, O.K.? I want you to have it. It suits you.' Taking her hand, he wrapped it around the little medallion, then pressed his own over it. 'It's just a trinket. To remember the New World by when you get home.'

'Will it bring me luck?' She met his eyes levelly, and he looked away quickly.

'Sure.'

'Then thank you, Tony.'

'Just wear it, right? For me.' Quickly, awkwardly, he reached forward and tilted her face up to him. 'Goodbye, Laura.' His lips brushed hers gently before she could move away. Then he bent and ruffled Alex's hair. ''Bye, little feller. You come back and see me some time, O.K.? And have a good trip. Both of you. Ah, Robert—can I have a word?'

The door behind him had opened, but Robert Wentworth did not come out. With a quick lift of his hand, a passing salute, he turned into the actor's study. Alex ran ahead for the stairs, waving his eagle's feather aloft, and Laura followed him more slowly, fingering the pendant.

On the stairs she paused, looking down at it. It was no trinket, despite what Tony had said. It was old, of heavy silver, embedded with brilliant blue torquoises, the best Navajo work. It was shaped like a circle, containing a strange device like a serpent; the edges of the silver were scratched with indecipherable characters. Laura knew what it was, she had recognised it the instant he gave it to her; she had seen one just like it that day in Taos, and innumerable modern cheap copies in every shop in the area. Did he think she didn't know? she thought to herself wryly. What Tony Graham had just given her was a Navajo charm; like the Egyptian scarab, the Moslem blue palm, it was a sign, a sign with one purpose—to ward off the evil eye.

She smiled to herself. So the doctor was a little superstitious, after all! More than she was, she said firmly to herself, and certainly more than he had admitted. From downstairs she heard the murmur of the two men's voices, and she hurried on up the stairs. She might not believe in its powers, but still, it was beautiful. She was glad of the present.

Alex had a light supper on a tray, and—for once—was eager for bed, too tired even for a story. Within half an hour of their going upstairs he was fast asleep, his face lying peacefully against his palm, his arm clutching his teddy bear.

In her room, Laura tried to rest, but she could not settle. The events of the day tangled in her mind, weaving and interweaving, and she knew that though she was tired her mind was nervous and alert. Tony Graham had not left, she saw, looking from the window and seeing his car still parked outside in the gathering twilight. It was Cissie's night off, so even if she went downstairs there would be no one to talk to—and that was what she wanted, she realised, feeling an odd sudden shaft of melancholy. A friend, someone she could pour everything out to, just the way it was, without worrying about being cautious or tactful. Her father. From nowhere the old grief stabbed at her, and she stood up impatiently. She would go for a swim, she thought. It was still warm. The water might relax her.

Pulling on a towelling wrap over her swimsuit, she slipped silently out of the house. From the study came the sound of voices still; no one saw her leave. She paused on the terrace, looking down into the shadowy garden, hesitating for a second—darkness was falling more quickly than she had expected. Then, suddenly, in the drawing room behind her, the lights were switched on; she heard voices, footsteps. The two men must be coming out on to the terrace.

Quickly, knowing only that for some reason she could not explain she did not want to see either of them, that she wanted to be alone, she slipped out of sight, padding silently down the stone steps to the garden in her rubber-soled shoes. She heard the French windows thrown back; light blazed out over the trees.

'Where is she now?' It was Robert Wentworth's voice.

'She's gone to rest, I think. It's all right.'

Laura froze in her tracks, suddenly incapable of movement.

'But why the hell did you take her there?' There was a muffled exclamation, the clink of a glass.

'I tell you I didn't know. How should I?'

'God!' A bottle was banged down on the table.

There was a pause, then Tony Graham's voice came clearly across the still air.

'You think it was the same woman?'

'Of course it was, damn it! She described her vividly enough. She'd seen her twice already. She was obsessed by her. She was going back to her that last day—I'm sure of it. She said she would. She wanted me to go. Where else would you be going on Route 88, for God's sake, unless you were going out of state?'

'Well, I didn't know that. You've got to believe that, Robert. If I'd had any idea . . .'

'It's your fault, damn it!' Robert's own voice was cold with anger. 'You left Laura alone there. You waltzed off. Though I must say I'm surprised you did.'

'Just what do you mean by that?'

'You know damn well what I mean. I saw you the first day you met, don't forget that. She may be an innocent, but I'm not!'

In the darkness below Laura felt her cheeks flame with colour. She knew she ought to move, go away out of earshot, or at least let them know she was there. But embarrassment trapped her; above her there was a brief tense silence. When they began speaking again, so they wouldn't hear her, then she would go, she thought desperately. There was a creak as if someone were lowering themselves into a chair; she tensed, ready to move, but the next words froze her to the spot.

'O.K., let's bring this whole thing out into the open, if that's the way you want it.' Tony Graham's voice was taut with anger. 'You're jealous, Robert. Why not admit it?'

'Jealous? Don't be so damned stupid!'

'It looks that way from where I'm sitting. Since you brought her here, you've been on my back day and night. You're working yourself into the ground to get this movie finished, just so you can whisk her away out of trouble. For God's sake, every time I asked to see her there was some goddamn excuse! What's eating you, Robert? Are you in love with her? Afraid to face it, is that it?'

'You're being ridiculous—and damned rude. I'm not discussing Laura with you . . .'

'You started in on all this. And I'm telling you you'd better face up to it.' Tony Graham's voice rose in anger. 'Especially if you're telling me the truth!'

'Oh, why?' Robert Wentworth's voice was so cold, so haughty, it was like ice in the air. Laura felt pain tighten in her chest, ache like tears behind her eyes. She could not move.

'Because she's in love with you.' Tony Graham's voice was even, quite calm now. 'And if you haven't noticed that then you're a bigger fool than I thought you. So . . .' Someone stood up; there was a brief silence. 'So you'd better ask yourself, Robert, what you're going to do about all this. It's a goddamn impossible situation you've gotten yourself into, don't you see that? She's a great kid, she's got a lot of pluck, I admire her . . . no, let me finish. But can't you see you're heading for trouble? She's the one who's going to get hurt in all this. What if she decides she's got to leave, because of what she feels? It's just the kind of thing she would do. What happens to Alex then? You realise how dependent he is on her now—God, the whole thing's a mess!'

There was a long silence. Below them, Laura bowed her head. Tears, hot against her skin, welled silently from her eyes and spilled on to her cheeks. Robert finally spoke; his voice was low, tight.

'Is that what you really think?'

'Not think, know. It's written all over her face, for God's sake! Are you blind or something? It's pathetic!'

'Why pathetic?' Robert's voice was sharp.

'Because she's not just a silly kid with an infatuation for the big movie star. If she were, we wouldn't be having this conversation. It's more than that. She's worth more than that . . .'

'Don't you tell me what she's worth!'

'Well, don't just smash up her life because you're so blind you can't see what's going on right in front of you, that's all. And don't try to kid me you're not attracted to her either . . .'

'You mind your own goddamned business!'

Both men were standing now; she could see their shadows, looming suddenly tall against the trees.

'It is my business. Alex is my business. And I just don't want Laura getting hurt . . .'

'For God's sake! You think I want to hurt her?'

'I don't think you want to, but I think you might. You break people, Robert, you can't help it. It's just the way you are. Look at Lydia . . .'

A glass smashed violently on the stones above her.

'Get the hell out of here! Now—before I throw you out!'

The sudden violence of the breaking glass freed her limbs of the paralysis that had held her there. Blindly she stumbled forward, not looking where she was going. Her foot struck one of the urns at the bottom of the steps; it crashed over, the noise immensely loud. On the terrace above there was a sudden silence. Uncaring now, Laura began to run, down the path, shrubs scratching at her legs, to the sanctuary of the pool.

When she reached it she came to an abrupt halt, her breath catching painfully in her chest, her whole body shaking. It was dark now; in a short while the moon would be rising. A light breeze lifted the branches of the trees, shifting them with a sound like whispers. Before her in the starlight the pool was a black rectangle, the surface of its water unruffled, unbroken, like glass. Not moving, she stared down into its blackness. Her hand lifted to her mouth with an odd involuntary gesture, as if to stifle a sob or a cry, although she made no sound, and although the movement was a reflex over which she had no control, she saw it, as if from outside her own body, with great clarity. She thought: *it's true: I love him.*

The admission brought a kind of calm, a steely painful peace. It hurt, to love someone who had just made it clear there was no hope of that love being returned: perhaps love hurt anyway, she thought, whatever the circumstances. But even so it was better than the evasions and pretences and excuses that had filled her mind for the past weeks. *I love him,* she thought, saying the words carefully, silently, spelling them out in her mind. Then, quickly throwing off the wrap she had put on, she dived into the water.

It was startlingly cold, icy on her hot skin. She knifed through it and then surfaced, gulping air, letting the water rush off her face, her hair, her arms in a shimmer of phosphorescence. She tossed back her wet hair, feeling the water sleek it close to her head, over her back, treading water. Then she began to swim, pushing herself to the limit of her strength, as if she were in a race, up to the far end of the pool, a swift ducking turn, then back, another turn, another length, and another, swimming as fast as she was able, her arms cleaving through the water.

She knew he would come to her, and he did. When she had swum nineteen, perhaps twenty lengths, and her heart was hammering in her chest, her breath coming fast, and she reached up to the steps to pull herself from the water, he was standing there, waiting. Wordlessly he handed her a towel, wrapped it carefully around her, so it enveloped her completely, and then gently led her across to two chairs set out before the changing pavilion. For a while he was silent, looking out across the darkness of the garden. Then, at length, he spoke.

'You heard,' he said quietly. 'Didn't you, Laura?'

'Yes.'

She expected reproach, but there was none. He sat quite still, his eyes shadowed from her, his face turned aside.

'I'm sorry,' he said finally. 'I should have preferred . . .' He broke off. 'I wish you hadn't gone to that place today.'

'Lydia had gone there?' She looked at him curiously, finding it suddenly simple to be direct.

'Yes. Twice.' He hesitated. 'Just as a tourist the first time; I don't know. I was working. I suppose she had time to kill.'

'And she saw that Indian woman, the one who . . .'

'Oh yes.' Robert paused. 'She told me about it. It . . . affected her deeply. She seemed to think the woman could give her some kind of answer. I don't know. She was going there again, I'm certain of it—the day of the accident.'

'I see.' Laura hesitated, looking at the dark averted profile. 'Do you know what the woman said to her?'

'Yes.' He turned to meet her eyes. 'But I'm not going to tell you.'

Laura looked away, a stab of pain shooting through her that, even now, he should keep his bond of secrecy with a dead woman. She drew in her breath, instantly ashamed of her own pettiness, and when she looked back at him, and saw the pain etched on his features, she felt a dart of compassion.

'Robert, she loved you, didn't she? Lydia?'

The circumstances were so odd, the conversation so unreal, as if it took place beyond all normal boundaries, that she found she could ask at last the question that had been in her mind so long, knowing he would accept it. And he did. Her words provoked no exclamation, no reaction.

'Yes,' he said quite levelly, 'she did.'

'Did your brother know?'

'Yes.'

'And Alex?'

'Possibly.'

He would tell her now, she thought. About Alex. But he didn't. To her surprise, he turned to her and took her hand.

'Laura,' he met her eyes, 'this concerns you—because of Alex?'

'Of course,' she said, aware she answered a little too quickly. 'I wanted to understand why he wouldn't speak. Whether it was something more than the accident itself . . .' Her voice trailed away.

'I see.'

His tone was flat, so devoid of emotion, that she turned to him impulsively.

'I'm sorry,' she said quickly. 'You must think me very prying, I didn't mean . . .'

'No.' He pressed her hand. 'You have a right to know. You're very close to Alex now.' He paused. 'And to me.'

Pain knifed through her heart; not close enough for you to tell me the truth, she thought. Not even that close.

'Laura.' He leaned towards her, his eyes searching her face. 'You'll have to be honest with me too, you know. I have to understand.' He paused, his voice suddenly awkward. 'You heard what Tony Graham said? About you. About your feelings?'

She nodded silently.

'Was he right?'

She could feel the tension in him now; it passed like a current from his hand to hers. She met his gaze miserably. If she said yes, if she admitted it, she knew what would happen. Robert would send her away, before Alex became even more reliant on her, before she could be seriously hurt. It was too late for that already, she thought, too late from the first night I met you. And all she knew, with a sudden lurch of fear, was that she would do anything, certainly lie, not to leave him.

'No,' she said.

He drew back. 'You're quite sure?' He hesitated, his eyes still searching her face. 'You wouldn't lie? There's no need, you know. Not between us now. We've gone beyond that, surely, and . . .'

'No.'

'I see.' He released her hand. 'Then he was imagining . . . all that? He was quite wrong?'

Laura turned her head away, fighting back the tears, terrified Robert would see them and suspect. She was not being convincing, she thought desperately, her mind whirling.

It did show on her face, in her eyes, she knew it. When he kissed her, he must have sensed it. She tried frantically to think of something she could say, anything, that would quell finally any doubts he might have.

'Quite wrong. He was quite wrong. I don't . . . I just . . .' She sighed. 'I . . . I find you attractive, I suppose, that's all.'

'All?' He gave a low laugh.

'Yes.' She stood up abruptly. 'So there's no danger of my being hurt. You don't have to worry about that. I'm sure it will pass—it does, doesn't it, that kind of feeling? It wouldn't even have started, I don't think, if you hadn't . . .'

She was speaking wildly now, she could hear her own lack of control, and she broke off.

'Kissed you?' With one swift easy movement he was beside her, very close.

'I suppose so . . .' She tried to turn away, but Robert reached out and caught her arm. As he did so the towel slipped from her shoulders and fell to the floor at her feet.

'I shouldn't have done that, then?' His eyes glittered at her in the darkness.

'No, I suppose not . . .' Desperately fighting the current of want for him that was starting to build in her body, she turned her face away.

'But I wanted to—very much. Graham was right about that. I am attracted to you, Laura. I . . .'

'Don't!' Quickly she reached up her hand to his lips, stopping his words. Instantly he caught it, imprisoning her wrist.

'It's not that simple, Laura.' His voice was low, roughened, suddenly urgent. 'It's so strong, I can't pretend it isn't there. All the time, even when I'm not with you . . . I know you feel it too. I can sense it. From the very first I could sense it.' He hesitated, looking down into her upturned face. 'I've . . . I've never known anything so powerful before.'

'Neither have I.' She spoke before she could stop herself. Instantly with a swift movement he drew her to him, locking his arms tight around her waist, pressing her close against his heart. He laughed softly.

'So what are we going to do then, you and I? When we go back to Marston? When we're alone together, when we both know . . .'

Her body stirred in his arms. No matter how she tried to force it down she could feel the pulse, the surge of desire for him rise, wave upon wave of it, through her body. He moved, so his strong hands were against the bare damp skin of her back, and she cried out involuntarily.

'You see?' He tilted her face up to him. 'What shall we do?'

'You could send me away.' She met his eyes.

'You could choose to go.'

Robert ran his hand up her bare back, cradling her head up to him, so she trembled in his arms.

'We could pretend . . . if we ignored it . . .' Her own voice sounded like a stranger's to her ears, husky, thick. 'If you never touched me . . .'

'Yes?' He smiled at her gently, mockingly, and very deliberately let his hand move in a long slow caress, around the long line of her throat, down to the curve of her breast.

'You think I could do that?'

'Yes—you must. You said the other night, when we drove out into the desert. You said then . . .'

'I was wrong, you know I was. You can feel it.'

'Oh, God! No, I . . .'

Robert moved so swiftly it was as if the force which gathered in her own body compelled him. When they were that close together, she thought blindly, it was like being in a force field that blotted out everything except the proximity of their bodies. They had to be closer; the compulsion to touch, to be touched, was as elemental as the pull of the earth, the attraction of magnetic poles. His hands tightened their hold against her bare back; with a rough movement he pulled her to him, pressing her body against him, so she felt him hard against her, the force of his arousal as unmistakable as if they were naked. The intimacy of that sudden knowledge, of his maleness, frightened her and heated her. She trembled, feeling her body sag against his, tilting her head back so that the warmth of his mouth met her throat. She heard herself gasp, her eyes closed. Everything was blotted out except the fire in her blood, the compulsion to seek his mouth, to assuage the fire with his kisses.

'You see?' His voice was broken, as uncontrolled as her own. For a brief second she opened her eyes and they looked at one another. Then with a deep sigh, he kissed her. The joining of their mouths, the warmth of his lips against hers, the deepness of his kiss brought release at first, a sudden peace that quieted the clamour in her blood. But it did not last; instead it built into a new demand, more insistent. She

felt her breasts strain against him, swell and harden under the
touch of his hand. She wanted more than this joining of their
mouths. Her body sang with the clarity of the want she felt,
and beside that want everything else fell away. There was no
morality, no time, no place.

'Dear God, Laura, I ...' His mouth was muffled again
against her throat.

Let it be now, she prayed silently and incoherently. *Here, on
the ground if need be ...*

And she reached up her hand to his face, as, opening her
eyes, she saw the moon suddenly clear, almost full pass out
from behind cloud, rising above the trees. Their branches
moved, with a light ripple like water. Breeze touched her skin.
As she reached for him her hand brushed her own throat, and
suddenly she froze. The abrupt tensing of her body
communicated itself to Robert; instantly he lifted his head,
looking down into her face, his eyes changing in a moment.
For a second she saw his face as she had never seen a man's
face before, clouded with the concentration of desire; then at
once it was alert.

'Laura? What's wrong?'

'My necklace.' She could hardly speak. 'The medallion I
was wearing. It's gone!'

He released her, his face hardening, and stepped back. She
knew at once what he was thinking: that her mind had been
elsewhere, even then, when he had been kissing her.

'No, please ...' She reached out a hand to him, but he did
not take it. 'I just realised then, a second ago. My hand
brushed my throat and I ...'

'You don't need to explain,' he said coldly. 'I quite
understand. It's the one Tony Graham gave you, presumably?'

She nodded.

'Then we'd better find it, hadn't we?'

How had he known that? she wondered, as he turned
abruptly away. Had he seen them together in the hall? Or had
the doctor perhaps told him? Even as the thought flashed
through her brain her eyes were dazzled. Robert threw a
switch by the poolside, and instantly the tiles, the surface of
the water gleamed with light. He turned back to her, his face
closed and unreadable, while she stood there awkwardly,
uncertain what to do, wanting to tell him what she had felt,
but afraid now, shy of him. In the light the scene that had just

taken place receded into unreality. The closeness she had felt, the sense that there were no barriers between them, evaporated into the night air.

'Well, where do you suggest we look?'

'I think . . . in the pool. I dived in, you see, and perhaps . . .' Her own voice sounded odd, forced. He gave a grimace of exasperation, and reached for the fastening of his shirt.

'No, please . . . I'll look. I'm already wet, don't . . .'

Before he could stop her she moved quickly to the edge of the water, then lowered herself very gently over the side, so that her body would create few ripples.

'No, Laura, wait!'

'It's all right—I'm sure it must be here.'

She launched herself into the centre of the pool, without pausing. Then taking a deep breath, she lowered her face into the water, opening her eyes, feeling the sudden sting of the chlorine. She moved slowly, hardly disturbing the water, her eyes searching the blue tiles at the bottom of the pool, confused by the shadows, the eddies. There were lights under the water, set in the walls of the pool. As her eyes grew accustomed to the water, she could see quite well. The deep end, she thought. That was where she had dived in. Perhaps there.

She took another breath, lowered her face again, scanning the blue tiles. They were amost the same colour as the turquoise of the medallion, she realised, it would not show clearly. And anyway she might have dropped it earlier, in the garden. Then suddenly she saw it. It was there, at the very edge of the pool, just under one of the lights, where water bubbled and eddied from one of the vents. She surfaced, air searing her lungs.

'I've found it!' she called, over her shoulder.

'No, Laura, wait . . .' She was just conscious that Robert had begun to run, up the side of the pool towards the deep end.

'It's all right—I can get it!' She took a deep breath and dived down. The water was deep here, deeper than she had realised. It took almost all her strength to force her body down against its pressure, and she knew that one breath would only just take her deep enough to reach it. She was nearly there. Almost . . . with one last kick of her legs she was down; her hand closed over the silver. She tugged, bubbles of air streaming from her mouth and nose. But it would not come away; something was holding it.

Then she saw what it was. The thin silver chain had caught in the grating. Delicately, fighting to retain the last breath in her lungs, Laura slipped her fingers along the chain and down. There; she had it. Her fingers closed on the chain, water bubbled up into her face from the vent. She turned her body in the water, and as she did so, her fingers stabbed with pain. She looked back down, in unbelief. Her hand was caught. The grating was narrow, and she must have . . . Blind terror suddenly swept over her in waves. She jerked her hand, knowing it must free itself. But it didn't. She couldn't move. She looked down; the medallion was there, perhaps an inch from her hand, its silver winking in the eddying light. Her fingers were trapped between two narrow bars of the grating. She stared, mesmerised, aware now only of the pain in her lungs and her head, the bursting pressure in her chest. She thought, *I must breathe.* She could feel blood behind her eyes, coming down over her vision like a veil, and the hurt receded as the blood came down. *She was right, the Indian woman,* she thought, with an odd detached composure. She stopped struggling when the water went black.

Robert freed her. He told her afterwards how. He made it seem very simple. Her fingers had not been jammed, he said, he had released them quite easily. She must have been pulling back at the wrong angle. As soon as he touched her hand it had come free. *You probably panicked, that's all,* he said later, lightly. And Laura did not disagree, though she knew he was wrong.

But all that came later, much later. When she came round it was to the sharp thrust of his hands against her sternum, the trickle of water from her mouth as her body sagged against him. And then the coldness of the tiles against her back, as he tilted her head and she felt his mouth cover hers, the breath of his lungs forcing life back into hers.

When she could breathe again, though the air smarted in her throat, he gathered her into his arms, wrapping her in the towelling jacket she had brought to the pool so her skin did not touch the cold wetness of his clothes. His face was dark with anger and incomprehension, and also something like fear.

'Laura, for God's sake, why did you do it? Why didn't you let me? Here.' With a quick gesture he bent and picked up the medallion and looped it over her neck. 'Wear it,' he said roughly. 'I didn't believe all that before, but now . . .'

'It's all right—please. It was just an accident . . .'

'Don't talk. And for God's sake don't argue!'

With an easy strength he lifted her into his arms and carried her up the path to the house. She leaned weakly against him, suddenly exhausted, all the fight gone out of her. She hardly saw where he was taking her as he shouldered her up the stairs and opened a door on the landing. It was only when he had lowered her on to a bed and switched on the lamp beside it that she saw she was in a strange room. His room, she realised, struggling to sit up, her eyes wide with anxiety.

'Don't move.' Roughly he pulled blankets around her, and pushed her back on the pillows. 'I'm getting some brandy. Lie still.'

He was only gone a few seconds. He returned with a bottle and a glass, and then held the cognac against her lips.

'Now,' he said sternly, 'drink this. Sip it slowly . . . that's it.'

The alcohol burned her throat; a second later she felt its warmth flood through her stomach, restoring magically a little of her strength. She smiled at him wanly.

'Don't talk. Finish it.'

Obediently she emptied the glass, and Robert took it from her and then stood looking down at her, his face stern.

'This is my fault,' he said finally, abruptly. 'I should never have brought you here.'

'No, please . . .' Laura leaned forward anxiously. 'It's not your fault at all. This could have happened anywhere. I was just stupid. I lost my head and . . .'

'I wasn't referring to the accident.' His dark eyes met hers, and instantly there hung in the air between them a shared knowledge. Their memories of the scene before she had dived into the water, of that physical need and proximity reverberated for a second in the space between them. She lowered her eyes and looked away.

When he spoke again his voice was rough and awkward.

'Well,' he said, 'one thing's clear anyway. We're leaving here—at once. Tomorrow.'

'But the film . . .' She stared at him.

'We finished the film today. It's over, wrapped. I should have told you earlier, but we . . .' he hesitated, and she saw a smile lift the corners of his lips, 'we got sidetracked. If one can put it like that.'

'I see.' In spite of herself, Laura felt her own lips curve into a smile, and at once his eyes darkened.

'Don't look at me like that,' he said sharply. 'I shan't be responsible for the consequences if you do.'

'I'm sorry.' She hesitated, suddenly confused, feeling the insidious pulse of desire start up again in her veins. 'I . . . I should thank you,' she said finally. 'You saved my life.'

He looked at her oddly, then he shrugged. 'You changed mine,' he said stiffly.

She stared at him. From nowhere came hope, sharp and clear like pain. Then it was gone. Alex, she thought dully. He just means because of Alex.

He hesitated for a moment, as if expecting her to say something, and when she did not he abruptly left the room without a word. When he returned she saw he was carrying her nightdress.

'You'd better put this on.' He gestured across the room to the bathroom. 'Make sure you're properly dry. You've had a shock and . . .'

'I'm quite all right.'

Feeling ridiculous, avoiding his eyes, Laura crossed the room and closed the door firmly behind her. Then she stripped off the wet swimsuit and rubbed her cold skin with one of his towels. It bore the scent of his skin, just faintly. Impulsively she hugged it against her, then pulled on her nightdress. When she came out again she saw that Robert too had changed. His wet clothes lay in a heap on the floor. He had pulled on jeans and a sweater.

'Right, now go and lie down.'

He gestured towards his bed, and she stared at him in astonishment, the blood coursing instantly from her neck to her cheeks.

'Don't worry, I shan't touch you. But I want you here, where I know you're safe. Just until we leave.'

Gently he took her hand and led her over to the bed, pulling the covers around her like a child. Then he lay down beside her. He slipped his hand under her shoulders, lifted her against him so her head rested in the crook of his shoulder. He smiled down into her anxious upturned face.

'Go to sleep, Laura.'

She was too tired to argue; she accepted the situation with the tranquillity of exhaustion. Instead, she closed her eyes, feeling the steady rise and fall of his chest against her cheek, feeling her own body stir, and then subside into quietude.

'Tomorrow we'll go back to Marston,' Robert said softly, when she was almost asleep.

'And then?' she asked, as he reached to turn off the light.

'Then? I don't know,' he answered.

I love you, she thought. But she said nothing, just resting her arm across his chest. After a little while, in the darkness, perhaps when he thought her asleep, she felt him take her hand. Sleepily, hardly awake, she opened her eyes. He was lying back, his eyes open, staring into the shadows of the room, the lines of his face sharply etched with exhaustion.

She never knew how long she slept. Several hours, certainly, for when she woke, suddenly, with a start, the first light of the day, thin, pearl-grey, just filtered through the curtains. She sat upright, instantly wide awake, all her senses alert. Beside her Robert murmured in his sleep; his hand clenched then relaxed against the pillow. Laura sat perfectly still, listening.

She had heard something; she knew it. Yet now the room, the house, was utterly silent. And cold. She shivered, suddenly afraid, feeling her heartbeat quicken; the fear she had felt in the pool returning to her.

Then she heard it again, muffled by distance, but quite clear. A thin, high-pitched wail. Then silence.

For a moment she could not move; fear paralysed her. Instinctively her hand reached for the medallion round her throat, clutching it, and as she did so Robert stirred in his sleep. His lips moved.

'Lydia,' he said.

In a second Laura was off the bed and across the room, had thrown back the door. From the passageway she heard it again, thin, rising in pitch, breaking off abruptly, like the cry of an animal in pain. Her room—it was coming from her room.

She broke into a run, her bare feet making no sound on the tiled floors. Along the corridor, down three steps, along again. It was darker here, for there were no windows, and she paused, hesitating. Her bedroom door was open.

For a moment blind terror possessed her. She pressed herself against the walls of the corridor, listening, her own breathing, the hammering of her heart, immensely loud in her ears. From the room beyond she heard a movement, a rustling. *She's come back, Lydia has come back!* Out of nowhere the thought winged its way into her brain and lodged there insanely, blotting out everything else.

She took a step forward, and her foot brushed against something warm and furry. She heard herself give a little cry of fright, then looking down, she saw what it was. It was Alex's teddy-bear. With an exclamation she bent and picked it up, clutching it to her. In that instant her courage returned. She stepped forward into the doorway.

The fierce protectiveness she felt then was so intense she knew she could have faced anyone or anything. But the room was empty. One window was open; a curtain flapped in the breeze; grey light striped the rugs on the floor.

Then she saw him. It was Alex, crouching by her empty bed, his face buried in the covers. In the instant she saw him, he turned and stared across the room, his face pale, wet with tears. Another cry, thin, choked as before, rose in his throat as she stood there. Before she could move, or speak, he was on his feet. He lifted his arms, and held them out to her stiffly. His lips moved silently; he took a step forward.

'Laura,' he said. 'Laura.'

For a moment Laura just stared at him, rooted to the spot. Then it was as if a great constriction lifted from her heart; an intense swift joy flooded her whole body, lit her face, a joy so intense it seemed to irradiate the room. In a second she was beside him, clasping him tightly in her arms.

'Alex. Alex, it's all right. I'm here, darling, it's all right . . .'

He buried his head against her breasts, clung to her tightly, his small hands gripping the cotton of her nightdress, his whole body shaken with choking sobs as, quite suddenly, he gave way completely to his grief.

Gently Laura lifted him, cradling him in her arms, and sat with him on her lap, rocking him back and forth, stroking his back, his hair, murmuring to him the banalities of comfort, until gradually, very slowly, the sobs grew weaker, the pauses between them longer, and his body quieted.

'There, Alex, there. It's all right. There was no need to be afraid. I'm here. Now . . .' very gently she tilted his face up to her, 'are there any more tears? Just one . . . let me wipe it away. There!'

Suddenly the room was quiet again. Alex's eyes met hers; she took his hands, and for a moment they just looked at each other. Laura saw his lips move silently, as if to frame a word, and she held her breath, trying to fight back the tension in case it communicated itself to him. Would he speak again? Or

had it just been the extremity of the moment? Would he go
back now into his old silent world? Even as the thought
passed through her mind his lips moved again. He frowned
slightly as a child does when concentrating on something.
Then he spoke. His voice was a little uneven in pitch, not
much more than a whisper.

'I thought you were dead,' he said. 'Like my daddy.'

'No, my darling. You silly boy, of course not!' Her arms
tightened around him. 'I'm here, look, look. Give me a good
pinch. See?'

He gave her arm a half-hearted prod; the ghost of a smile
touched his lips, though his eyes were still uncertain.

'Your bed was empty . . .'

'Yes, but I wasn't far away. I . . . I was talking to your
Uncle Robert, just down the corridor.'

That would have to do, she thought, hoping he would
accept it. Alex hesitated, thrusting his lower lip out
obstinately.

'I had a bad dream,' he said at last. 'I dreamed you was
dead, Laura.'

She hugged him to her, fighting off the knowledge that he
should dream something so close to what might have been the
truth.

'It was just a dream, Alex, that's all. Sometimes one has
bad ones, sometimes good ones. And they both go away in
the morning.'

'You won't go away? Laura?'

His small hand gripped her sleeve tightly, his face twisted
up to hers intently. Pain shot through her like a knife; she
fought desperately not to let him see the hesitation in her face,
but before she could speak, someone else answered for her.

'No, she won't, Alex. Of course not.'

The voice was quiet, utterly determined. They both swung
round. Robert was standing in the doorway of the room,
watching them. Alex hesitated, looking from one to the other.

'Not ever?'

This time it was Robert who was silent, Laura who
answered. Two pairs of identical dark eyes burned into hers,
and she smiled gently.

'Not while you want me,' she said.

'Laura . . .' The man and the boy both spoke at once. Then,
both glancing at each other, both breaking off, Alex began to
smile, and Robert gave a sudden low laugh of triumph and

happiness. He held out his arms awkwardly, and Laura saw the glint of tears in his eyes. Alex hesitated only for a second, then in one swift movement he was across the room and swept up high in the man's arms.

Happiness drew Laura towards them instinctively; Robert reached out and clasped her hand. All three were drawn into a rough embrace, none speaking. Laura clasped the hard hand that held hers tightly, tears and laughter fighting in her face.

After a little while the grip on her hand loosened, and Robert tilted Alex's head back so he could look him in the face.

'Well now,' he said, and Laura marvelled at the control in his voice, 'I think we should all go and get some breakfast, don't you?' He paused. 'Alex, what would you like?'

Alex hesitated. He glanced at Laura, and his lips curved into a smile.

'I'd like waffles,' he said firmly. 'And syrup. And milk.'

Laura laughed, and Robert grimaced.

'Ugh!' he said cheerfully. 'At three o'clock in the morning? What a mixture! However . . .' he turned to the door, 'waffles it shall be.' He reached out for Laura and drew her after them. 'And Laura had better cook them, don't you think, Alex?'

They made an odd group, Laura thought, as she busied herself in the kitchen. The tall dark man, barefoot, in need of a shave, his face drawn with strain and tiredness, his eyes alight with happiness. The little boy, his face still blotched from his crying, his voice growing stronger and more confident with each sentence he uttered. And herself, still in her nightdress, her hair bedraggled from the pool, trying to remember how to make waffles and finding the simple recipe had flown out of her head, and that the most simple movement, the lifting of a cup, made her hands shake.

They weren't the best waffles she'd ever made, she thought wryly, but nobody seemed to mind in the least, and they all three ate with suddenly voracious appetites. In fact, the whole meal became a little hysterical, with everyone talking at once, and laughing, and knocking things over, and picking them up again. And when Robert said quite casually, 'Would you like a ride in an aeroplane today, Alex, because I thought we might all go back to Marston?' and Alex's face lit up with new excitement, and he and Robert launched themselves on a long discussion about altitudes and automatic pilots and a million terms so technical they made her mind swim, she was able at last to draw back a little, and just to watch them, the man and the boy, both so alike, both so charged with happiness.

At about four, the kitchen door suddenly opened to reveal Cissie, wrapped majestically in an enormous yellow quilted dressing gown, her hair bound up in a turban, her eyes round with astonishment.

'Land sakes!' she said finally. 'And I thought we'd got burglars!'

'Good morning, Cissie,' said Alex, with a mischievous grin. Cissie's mouth set.

'Good morning, honey,' she said firmly, then exited rather abruptly in the direction of the pantry.

The three left at the table looked at one another in perplexity. There was a sudden silence, broken at last by the sounds of noisy weeping, muffled ineffectively by the pantry door. Alex's eyes rounded. He looked at Robert, then at Laura. Fortunately, the storm of weeping was loud but brief. Shortly afterwards, Cissie reappeared, bearing herself with dignity. She gave Alex a broad wink.

'I allus say, honey, that when you're real happy, there's nothing like a good cry,' she pronounced.

'I can talk now, Cissie,' Alex said proudly.

'Sure you can, honey, and I'm pleased. Real pleased.' She gave a gulp, which she managed to turn into a sniff. She glared at Laura. 'And them waffles was burned,' she said fiercely, disappearing as rapidly as she had come.

Alex gave a small sigh of contentment, as Laura and Robert glanced at each other in a second of happy complicity.

'I like them burned,' he said decisively. 'They're good with the edges all crunchy.'

CHAPTER TEN

AFTER that their departure was less a leavetaking than a triumphal progress. The morning passed in a flurry of activity; the telephone never stopped ringing, the very air of the house seemed warm with happiness and congratulations. Robert was a changed man. Happily Laura watched him; all the terseness, the formality, the strain of the past weeks seemed to have left him. He was again as he had been in England—debonair, relaxed, high-spirited—the shadows had gone from his face.

On all sides there was activity. A secretary arrived from the film company, and stationed herself on one telephone to fix all the travel arrangements. Robert stationed himself at another, calling Marston, briefing his housekeeper and her husband, who would fetch them from the airport. They would go first class to New York, Concorde to London, then take a small private Cessna on to the Midlands. Cissie rushed about in a fervour, plying everyone with food at every opportunity. Silvana, the Mexican maid, quietly got on with the packing. Amid fierce protests Alex was put back to bed, to sleep until the time came to leave. Laura was hugged, kissed, congratulated on all sides. The nurses brought her a posy of flowers, Winston came bursting in and lifted her off her feet in a bear-hug, Cissie had another cry, this time on Laura's shoulder, while Laura herself began to feel more and more lightheaded with exhaustion and happiness. Once, Robert came bursting out into the hall.

'Where's my address book?' he demanded wildly, seeing Laura.

'In your hand,' she said gently.

'Oh, so it is,' he said, scooped her up in his arms, planted a kiss firmly on her lips, then disappeared again. Cissie witnessed this, and burst into tears again.

By ten-thirty, they were all packed in the Lincoln. By noon in the 747 on their way to New York, by afternoon in Concorde. Alex, having been given a guided tour of the cockpit and having described the instrument panel to anyone who would listen three times, was fast asleep, curled up on the row of seats reserved especially for this purpose, and Robert was ordering champagne. In spite of her tiredness, his gaiety infected Laura. Together they laughed and talked, going over and over again the scene in her bedroom, the moment when Alex had first spoken. It was as if all the darkness, the worry, the strain between them had gone, she thought happily, looking into his eyes. It was as if, miraculously, events had tipped them all towards disaster, and then—at the last moment—they had escaped into the light. Even her fears of the night, the remembrance of her accident in the pool had no power to affect her. They had vanished with the dawn, with Alex's first words.

The gods are with us, she thought happily. It was an old phrase of her father's.

'You must try and sleep, Laura.' Robert touched her hand lightly, and instantly the casual touch flashed from nerve-ending to nerve-ending.

'I'll try,' she said quietly. 'You should too, you know.' She smiled up at him. 'Neither of us got much sleep last night . . .' *And when you slept, you dreamed of Lydia*, she thought, but she said nothing, though the memory hurt her. Perhaps he did always.

'I can't sleep.' He gave her a sideways glance, half mocking, lit with the old flirtatiousness, and instantly she felt herself weaken, respond. 'I need my arms round you when I sleep. I discovered that last night.'

'Then you'll have to undiscover it, won't you?' she said crossly. Why did he have to be so damnably charming?

'Possibly.' Before she could move he had slipped his arm under her shoulders, so her head rested against him. 'On the other hand, possibly not. No, don't move.' His grip on her tightened, and she gave up the struggle. 'This is a positively avuncular embrace—even you can't object to it. Now, go to sleep—I have to make plans.'

'Plans?' Laura rested her head sleepily in the crook of his arm, his closeness at once relaxing her. 'Plans about what?'

He smiled. 'Oh, this and that,' he said airily. 'Go to sleep, darling.'

Her hands clenched; a dart of pain mixed with want instantly shot through her body, from her heart to her womb. Dear God, she thought, closing her eyes, hoping against hope that he did not sense her reaction, does he have any idea of his power—that he can do that to me? Just with one word.

Against her closed lids the events of the past day and night swirled before her, mixing, then separating. The newspaper office; the Indian woman; the conversation overheard on the terrace; the suffocation of water; the cry in the night. The images receded and advanced, made as vivid as hallucinations by her exhaustion. But no matter how they circled and re-circled they came back always to one image—of Robert's embrace, first by the pool, then, in that grey light in her room, when for a long moment he had held her and Alex against his heart.

Let go, she thought. If she was to stay, and she must stay for Alex's sake, just as Robert had said, and she had

promised, then she knew she must disengage. There could be
no more contact between her and this man, no matter how
much they each might want it. She knew what it must lead to,
inevitably, and she knew what would be the result; for her,
unhappiness; and for Alex, more destruction. *No*, she
thought, though her cheek still rested above the measured
beat of his heart. *No*. And she fell asleep.

It was the last thought she was conscious of; the first thought
that came to her on waking. All the way back in the little
Cessna plane, in the car from Birmingham airport, she made
disjointed plans. To be cheerful, apparently unaffected, but
firm. To stay out of his reach; to be alone with him as little as
possible. Never to betray, with a look or a glance or a gesture
what she felt.

And so, when they came to Marston at last, in the late spring
evening, and the great car sped up the sweeping drive, when the
housekeeper flung back the door, and Robert bundled them all
into the hall and turned to her, his face alight with happiness,
and said, 'Alex, Laura, We're home!' her heart turned over, but
she drew back a little and said nothing.

That was the hardest moment, for—just for a second—it
was as if they were a family, as if she were his wife, as if this
were really her home. After that it was easier, for again there
was a flurry of activity. A light supper for Alex, unpacking,
his excitement at rediscovering his old room, and the need to
quieten and relax him. Once he was in bed, and at last
peacefully asleep, there was dinner alone to be got through,
but even that was not too difficult, for there was the
housekeeper, Mrs Bowles, constantly bustling in and out,
repressing with difficulty her excitement at their return, and
her obvious wish to gossip.

'I've put your coffee in the morning-room, sir,' she said
when she finally withdrew. 'That chimney in the drawing
room's smoking again. And you'd be needing a fire in the
evenings, I thought . . .'

And then, when they went into the morning room, it was
easiest of all. Because as soon as Robert opened the door for
her, Laura knew the room was different. The portrait of
Lydia had gone. It had been replaced with a nineteenth-
century seascape, conveniently large, but not quite large
enough. The pale marks on the wall where the portrait had
been still showed, at the edges.

He gestured, awkwardly, seeing the direction of her gaze.

'I thought, you see, because of Alex, it might be better . . .'

'I'm sure you're right,' she said, keeping her voice brisk, and they changed the subject.

They drank their coffee and talked, with only a few awkward pauses. At the first possible opportunity she stood up, saying she was tired, she must sleep. At the door, she shut her heart to the expression of confusion and disappointment on his face.

'Goodnight.'

'Goodnight then, Laura.'

She closed the door firmly behind her, only paused on the stairs. She was glad he had had the portrait moved, she thought sadly. Glad because it only confirmed something she had sensed from the first day she had come here, and now fully recognised. That the house was permeated by Lydia's presence, that her spirit still ruled its rooms and corridors. The absence of her portrait did not weaken her hold, it strengthened it. And it strengthened Laura's resolve.

In the nursery she looked down at Alex. *Her* son, she thought. Just as the man downstairs was her man. She fingered the silver medallion around her neck, and for the first time that day felt at peace. Yesterday, by the pool, she had stepped across some invisible barrier, and she had been warned.

She wouldn't do it again, she thought. For Alex's sake. Perhaps even a little for Robert's. *Rest, Lydia*, she thought, then, mocking herself for such superstitious fancies, she went into the room next door, and quickly, easily, as if she had made her peace with something, fell asleep.

A week passed. It was a week of extraordinary calm. When Laura looked back on it afterwards the days fused in her memory into one long unbroken period of happiness. The weather was warm, clement, with none of the unpredictability of spring. Each day the sun shone; in memory after, it coloured her images of that time; they were all washed with gold. In the garden it was possible to mark the passage of time precisely, in the unfurling of each leaf, in the pale green shoots of bulbs that inched their way above the dark earth. But in retrospect the time seemed still, unmeasured, endless.

They explored the house and the park together, the three of them. They went riding. They had picnics. With the help of

Harry, Mrs Bowles looking on and proffering a stream of advice, they built the promised tree-house in the wide low branches of a cedar. Never once did they leave the confines of the estate. It bounded them; they were content. It was like the Garden of Eden, Laura thought once, wryly, not speaking what she thought.

Alex's confidence grew each day. His voice grew strong and unwavering, without the old hesitations. He never spoke of the silent time, or of the past, and nobody questioned him. Laura herself felt happy, so happy it sometimes frightened her. She had not, she felt obscurely, earned the right to such content. Once, twice, perhaps a few times, she felt the old ache of want for something more, for a promised land glimpsed and now gone, but those feelings quickly left her. And she was cautious. As much as possible she avoided being alone with Robert, taking secret pleasure just in watching him, noting his quick negligent strength, the way he rode a horse as if the animal were part of his own body. Sometimes, it was true, she sensed him looking at her, knew he too was watchful. Once or twice, glancing up at him, she caught on his face an expression that made her heart contract with pain, a kind of puzzlement, a guarded concern. Yet he made no approach to her, no overture, no attempt to take them back to the intimacy of their last night in New Mexico. He seemed not cold, but without desire, as if he sensed the invisible line she drew around herself, and accepted it. Perhaps his feelings had changed, passed, she thought once. Though she knew every time he was close to her, every time his hand brushed her arm, every time she felt his breath against her skin, that hers had not.

The feeling was there still, just below the surface; one touch, one word, and it would have flowered in her blood as powerfully as ever. She felt only relief, she told herself, that the touch, the word, the gesture, never came. All the same, she knew he watched her.

One night, after dinner, when they sat together in the drawing room listening to some music, she heard, as the record finished, a different sound, the soft pulse of falling rain. Moving to the curtains she looked out into the garden. It was dark, she could see nothing against the panes except the reflection of the room behind her. But she could hear it, the wash of the rain; the weather had broken. Robert moved behind her. For a moment, as his hand came up to move the heavy curtains further aside, his arms encircled her, without touching. Instantly she flinched. He turned and they stood for a moment, neither speaking, just looking at one another, the little space between them suddenly clamorous with a force which was unspoken. The silence seemed to hum with power, like the reverberation of a bowstring after the release of an arrow.

When, fighting not to show the sudden alarm she felt, Laura said she must go to bed, and mumbling an excuse about tiredness turned away, he did not stop her. He did not even answer.

The next morning she woke early, her mind restless, and knew at once she would not go back to sleep. So, quickly, she pulled on some old clothes, boots, trousers, a thick sweater and jacket, and slipping out through the silent house, let herself into the garden.

She stood there quietly, breathing the fresh moist air, watching the sky grow lighter in the east, and she felt herself grow calmer. The earth was pungent after the night's rain; the air smelled like violets. The seasons were at a point of change; she could sense the coming spring, the promise of summer.

She thrust her hands deep in her pockets and looked at the garden before her, at the trees just coming into bud, the first bulbs spearing the dark earth near her feet. For the first time since they had returned she felt at peace, completely so. So that, even when her gaze fell on the blue face of the clock above the door, and she realised that it said two, the hour Lydia had died, and that Robert must have stopped the hands there, for that reason—even then, though the realisation hurt her sharply, she could accept it.

She stood still, thinking, listening to the silence, letting the breeze blow against her face. She did not hear footsteps, nor the door open, but she knew suddenly, with some sixth sense, that Robert had joined her. Slowly she turned, meeting his eyes; without speaking, he took her arm, pressing her hand against his heart, and led her along the paths between the yew hedges. They walked in step, silently, until they came out on to the terrace where they could look down to the lake. Silently they stood looking at the calm grey water, the sky fading rose behind it, the air above the water hazy. In the half-light a heron took flight; its great grey wings beating soundlessly. It veered towards them, then away, disappearing like a ghost.

Robert covered her hand with his own, briefly.

'You couldn't sleep, then?' he said.

'No,' she said quietly.

'Neither could I.'

That was all. He said nothing more. Afterwards, when she thought about that moment, again and again, replaying it in her mind with a feverish anxiety, Laura thought her memory must have played some trick with her: he must have said something more, he must have, the moment seemed full of speech, and yet they had said nothing.

After a while, Robert still holding her hand pressed against him, they turned and went back to the house. Outside the doorway, under the clock, their feet scrunched on the gravel, and he let go her hand. It was as if the noise, the gesture, fractured the moment, splintered it; she felt something sure within her disintegrate, and was in the instant embarrassed, hesitant, anxious only to get away.

She turned to the door, but he stopped her.

He would take her out to dinner that night, he said. They couldn't stay like prisoners in this house for ever, it was ridiculous. Alex was perfectly well, Mrs Bowles would babysit.

'But . . .'

'Wear that white dress we bought in London,' he told her. 'You should. You never have. I'd like to see you in it.'

Then he strode off, and did not look back, and Laura went indoors to wake Alex.

She wore the dress; it was like a Greek tunic. She washed her hair, then brushed it dry and let it hang, full and black, over the pale gold of her shoulders. Alex said she looked beautiful; Mrs Bowles was warm and full of compliments.

'You go off, my dear, and have a lovely evening,' she said. 'I'll be here. You've no cause to go worrying. We'll be all right, shan't we, Alex?'

Laura trembled a little when she went downstairs. Robert waited for her at their foot, watching her come down, tall and dark in a black evening suit. His eyes travelled from her face to her feet, then back again to her face. She brushed her hair nervously aside; but he said nothing.

He took her to the restaurant near Snowshill where they had gone that first day for lunch. Hugh Clancy greeted them warmly, and gave them a table in the corner of the dining room where they were shielded from view. The meal was delicious. Robert seemed relaxed.

He was witty, charming, courteous, and his eyes never left her face. Laura had the impression, though, that his real attention was elsewhere; as if there were something he wanted to say, and could not bring himself to speak. So, gradually, the pleasure she felt, the enjoyment, began to desert her. Nervousness started up within her from nowhere, followed by an irrational lurch of suspicion. He was leading up to something, suddenly she felt sure of it; that was why they had come here. There was something speculative in his gaze that frightened her.

She stared at him; the room was blurring, she was suddenly seeing only his features with the clarity of a photographic close-up; the dark watchful eyes, and—as if he sensed her sudden awareness—their refusal to meet hers.

'Have you seen who's just come in?'

'I'm sorry?' She stared at him stupidly, her mind whirling, trying to fix on his words.

'I said, look behind you. Discreetly.'

His manner was perfectly normal; he seemed to find her confusion amusing. She turned, following his gaze. A woman had just come in, with a man she did not recognise. She was wearing a scarlet dress; as Laura turned she looked up, and—in the moment of being seated—paused. It was Zara.

For a second their eyes met, then Laura turned away.

Robert pushed his glass away from him.

'We'll go now, I think,' he said, and stood up.

Before she could move he was beside her, and had drawn back her chair. His arm circled her waist.

Laura stood up in confusion, aware of eyes turned in their direction, a buzz of conversation, then a discreet English turning away of heads that did nothing to disguise palpable curiosity. She knew her cheeks flamed with colour. As if deliberately, Robert led her out past Zara's table, not looking once to left or right, making no acknowledgement. His arm was still circling her waist; she could feel the material of his sleeve burning against the bare skin of her back.

'We'll go home now, darling,' he said, just as they passed Zara's table.

When they reached the house it was in darkness; just one light burned in the hall. At once Laura turned to the stairs, but before she could make her planned speech of polite thanks, Robert took her hand and led her into the morning room, switching on the lamps.

'I'll get us a drink.' He hesitated. 'Or coffee. Would you like some coffee? I want to talk to you.'

She felt her heart lurch.

'Coffee,' she said. 'I'll make it . . .'

'No, I shall. You wait here.'

He left her, his footsteps echoing down the passageway to the kitchen. Laura looked around her nervously. This, of all the rooms in the house, was the prettiest, and the one she now most disliked. It was a little too pretty, it was partly that; it had a soft femininity absent from the formal grace of the other rooms. But it was not just that, not really that. It was the room in which she felt most conscious of Lydia's presence.

Irritated with herself, she forced her eyes away from the marks on the wall where Lydia's portrait had hung. She wandered over to the bookshelves, forcing herself to read the titles. The books might have been Lydia's, might not. Abstractedly she looked at their spines: Dickens; Flaubert; Woolf; Donne; Byron; Chekov. They told her nothing. The house had standard works, that was all; how long he took to make coffee! Then she turned back, staring: Byron. Her hands shaking a little, she reached for the book. A blue binding; the Oxford edition; the one in the portrait.

She opened it, almost dropping it in a sudden excess of nervousness. There was an inscription in the front, written in a large clear back-sloping hand. 'To Robert, from Lydia, with my love. Page 77.' There was a date, some eight years previously. The book tilted in her hands; Laura almost dropped it. Impatiently she turned the pages. Page 77 contained several poems; one was marked with a thick scored line down the side; she had time only to read the first line: *She walks in beauty, like the night.* The pages riffled under her fingers, although the air in the room was quite still. Hearing Robert's footsteps, she quickly replaced the book in the shelves, and turned away guiltily. *She walks . . .* She turned to the window, and as Robert opened the door, the tray tilting dangerously in his hands, she pulled the heavy curtains across the glass, blocking out the darkness of the garden, the moon that rose, a narrow crescent, over the cedars.

'Proper coffee,' he said. 'Aren't you impressed?'

His words tugged her back to normality. Instantly she felt

foolish; now that the curtains were closed the room was warm, without threat. She sat down, carefully choosing a chair, not the sofa, so he could not sit next to her, and watched him as he busied himself with cups, coffee, milk, sugar. When he had finished he sat down opposite her, his attitude one of complete relaxation. He loosened his tie; stretched, all his movements easy, elegant, with that sense of contained power that never left him; his eyes were watchful. For a while they talked; banalities. The food they had eaten; the obvious success of Hugh Clancy's restaurant. But the conversation was stilted, awkward, a papering over of cracks. Eventually Robert leaned back.

'I hear Zara's marriage has broken up,' he said, his voice casual. 'Hugh told me.'

She stared at him. 'Oh no, surely not! But that's sad. I mean . . .'

He shrugged. 'Perhaps. Predictable, though.'

'Yes. But the children . . .' Her voice tailed away. Suddenly the memory of Samantha and Jessy in the nursery came back to her.

Do people live happily ever after? In real life? Will Mummy and Daddy?

I'm sure they will, darling.

Her heart turned over; what right had she had to lie? she thought suddenly, fiercely. She should have told them the truth.

'Laura?'

With difficulty she turned back to face him, her mind still far away.

'Tell me.' He paused, seemed to hesitate. 'Have you ever loved anyone? Been in love?'

She looked away, pain and confusion locking around her heart. There was a silence, and she knew it was impossible to avoid an answer.

'Perhaps once.' She swallowed. 'Yes, I think—once.'

'And what happened?' He was quite still, regarding her intently.

'Nothing happened.'

'I see.' He looked down at his hands. 'And so it passed, did it, this feeling?'

'No.' She laced her own fingers in her lap.

He sighed, then leaned forward. 'So, what went wrong? Won't you tell me, Laura?'

'It wasn't returned,' she said, in a small flat voice. When he didn't answer her she glanced at him nervously, but his face was unreadable.

'I see,' was all he said.

Laura drew in her breath, gripped her palms with her nails.

'And you?' she asked, meeting his eyes, feeling her nerve return to her, determined, suddenly, to challenge him as he had challenged her. Would he tell her, now, about Lydia?

'Once.'

'And did it pass? Your feeling?'

Instantly she saw his mouth tighten with anger; his eyes glinted.

'No.'

There was a silence; Laura was the first to look away.

'Well, why don't you go on?' he said at last, his voice harsh and sarcastic. 'It was I who began this catechism, but since you seem determined to finish it, why don't you? Why don't you ask me, Laura, what happened?'

'What happened?' She had to force the words out, feeling her heart grow small and cold and tight within her. *I know what happened, more or less,* she thought, and knew, in that moment, that she could bear anything except to hear the details.

'Not a great deal.' His voice was cold, and Laura felt her cheeks flush with anger; she raised her head abruptly. Was that how he described the birth of his child, the pain and destruction afterwards?

'So, what went wrong?' Her own voice sounded strange in her ears, accusatory, cold. He gave her a hard little smile.

'The circumstances,' he said, 'were not propitious.'

His voice was mocking, as if he chose the stiff evasive phraseology deliberately, but the expression of pain was suddenly so dark in his eyes that she answered him without thinking.

'I'm sorry,' she said gently. 'I'm sorry. That it should have been . . . like that.'

And she was, she thought. Though it went against her whole heart, her whole mind, most morality, she was. However wrong it might have been, this man and Lydia, she could not find it in her to condemn them. How could she, she thought miserably, turning her face away, when she knew herself the power of an identical emotion? It was as if he read her thoughts.

'Aphrodite,' he said, making his voice light, and yet not convincing. 'The Greeks were right, don't you think? To make her a giver and a taker. A benefactress and a killer. And Eros, her son—a blind boy shooting his arrows into the air arbitrarily. How solemn we are tonight!'

His tone was the escape clause she sought; she took it instantly.

'Yes, we are,' she said firmly, moving to get out of her chair, forcing herself to sound, as he had done, mocking. 'It's very late, and we shouldn't be having this conversation at all, and I . . .'

'On the contrary, I intended us to have this conversation.' His voice, lazy now, almost flippant, froze her movements dead. He paused. 'Perhaps not quite this conversation.. But more or less.'

She sat arrested, unable now to leave, staring up at him, her mind suddenly paralysed. She had been right, she thought, earlier that evening, she had been right. He had been leading up to something. Perhaps he wanted her to go, to leave. He was just making sure that she understood his feelings, and then . . .

'Laura.' He stood up abruptly, and moved away from her, his back turned to her now, so she could not see his face. 'I want to ask you something.' He paused, as if awkward, then turned back, his manner one of agitation. 'It's been in my mind for some time. And then tonight, when I heard about Zara . . . What do you think about marriage?' If he saw her reaction, he gave no sign of it, but pressed on, very rapidly. 'I mean, in what circumstances should two people get married, do you think?'

She stared at him, knowing her face had gone white, unable to answer.

'Well, come on,' he said brusquely. 'You must have thought about it. Women do, or so I'm told. I mean, should it be a romantic thing, propelled forward by intense physical feeling, the way it always is in novels? A blow to the heart, a burning of the loins? You know the sort of thing, presumably?'

The sarcasm in his voice stung her; she looked away.

'Well, if not that, what? A sober considered decision? A pragmatic resolution? Two people find they get on together well enough, that they might as well throw in their lot together for eternity? Come on, what do you think?'

'I think . . .' She fought to keep her voice even. Then the

truth, angry in her heart, rose to her lips. 'I think that . . . you would love in one way first, afterwards in others. That you would be in love, and then you would love. Learn to love. The two things together. And that the being in love—that—would be a kind of premonition, a promise of the future.' She paused. 'I think, for marriage, you would need both kinds of love.'

'I don't agree at all.' His voice cut coldly across her words; pain shot through her that he should so stamp down on her when she tried at last to tell him what she felt.

'You don't?'

'No, I don't.' He turned away. 'I think, as far as marriage is concerned, romantic love is irrelevant, immaterial. That kind of love is at best transitory and generally a delusion—lust delayed. It's less frequent, you'll notice, in a permissive age. In my experience it's usually quickly cured, with coupling.'

The oddness of the word, the bitter distaste with which he uttered it, and his frankness—no man had ever spoken to her like that before—made her cheeks flood with colour. She lowered her head, furious with herself, furious with him, seeing now exactly what he had meant when he spoke of a shabby affair. A kiss meant one thing to her, another to him, she thought. It was as well to understand that.

'Laura.' His voice was gentler, as if he understood her reaction. 'Don't you see what I'm trying to say?' He paused. 'It's just that I think—have thought—that marriage is best approached quite differently, more rationally. Look at Zara and Michael, for God's sake—hopeless! Doomed from the first—it's obvious to anyone. But if marriage were based on esteem, mutual regard . . .' He hesitated. 'Respect, friendship.'

'It doesn't sound very romantic.'

'It isn't very romantic. That's why it might work. Don't you see, Laura . . .' He moved quickly taking her hand, drawing her to her feet, compelling her to look at him. 'Then it might last, don't you think?'

She stared at him, fixed by the expression in his eyes. It was one almost of pleading.

'I don't think you believe that,' she said at last in a low voice, 'any more than I do.'

'I do believe it.' His voice was fervent, almost desperate. He paused, meeting her eyes, holding her hand with a sudden curious formality. 'It's why I want you to marry me, Laura.'

'*What?*' She stared at him, feeling her blood go cold, shock and pain gripping her heart.

'I want you to marry me,' he repeated obstinately, not letting go of her hand.

'*No!*' She turned her head away with a sharp little gesture.

'Why not?' He let go her hand, and stepped back a pace, watching her still with that old mocking expression, the old detachment, and she hated him for it in that moment.

'Why not? It's obvious why not. I don't . . .' She broke off. 'We don't love one another.'

'I care for you.' He hesitated. 'Far more important, I like you. I respect and admire you.'

'So you said once before,' she cried bitterly.

'Well then, you have proof of my constancy.' He smiled, and she could have hit him across the face, the pain that blazed in her heart was so acute.

'Laura, listen.' He reached for her hand, as she drew it angrily away. 'I understand your feelings. I honour them. I'm not asking you to love me, please understand that. You're very young. You're truthful. I have no illusions . . .' He broke off. 'I don't want to burden you with some boring protestation of undying love, which in any case you wouldn't believe. But you like me, I think. We get on well together. We're happy together—aren't we? I could offer you some things—a home. I would take care of you. I wouldn't demand . . .' He hesitated.

'Wouldn't demand what?' Laura stared at him angrily, feeling the tears start behind her eyes.

'I wouldn't expect . . .' He spoke measuredly, choosing his terms. 'I wouldn't expect you to love me, not in the sense of which we spoke. I quite understand . . . you've made it quite clear. That's out of the question.' He shrugged. 'So be it.'

'Why don't you say what you mean?' Her eyes blazed at him angrily. 'I know why you're suggesting this. It's because of Alex, isn't it? You don't want a wife, you want a mother for Alex!'

He recoiled; it was as if she had hit him. 'You're already a mother to Alex,' he said.

'But I'm not!' The pain she felt was making her voice break. 'I'm not his mother, I'm his nurse. Hired by you, fired by you, if need be. I came here, and I could leave. And that's it, isn't it?' She stared at him. He had gone white; he looked angry, yet also more defenceless than she had ever seen him, and she

knew with absolute certainty in that moment that she was
right. Suddenly her anger broke, left her. She looked at him
for a long moment and her heart contracted within her. All
this, she thought. All this; he would go this far, to protect, to
help Alex. Pity rose up in her; the wish, in spite of everything,
not to hurt him further. She sighed. 'Robert,' she said, her
voice suddenly gentle, 'there's no need for this. Can't you see?
I shan't leave Alex. You have no worries on that score. As
long as he wants me here, I'll stay. Do you imagine that now,
just because he's well again. I'd walk out on him, leave? Of
course not!' She turned away, her voice suddenly dull. 'I'll
stay. You don't have to invent ways to keep me.'

'I don't want that.' His voice was tight, obstinate. 'I don't
want you here as a nurse—a child's nurse. I want you here as
my wife.'

'No.' She turned her head away, hoping he would not see
the pain in her eyes. 'It's impossible.'

'It's perfectly possible, damn it!' With a sudden fierce
gesture that took her totally by surprise he reached for her
arm and dragged her roughly round to face him. Laura
caught her breath; with one movement he had brought them
close, closer than they had been since they came back to
England. One hand was pressed against the bare skin of her
back; the other, with a fierce grip, imprisoned her arm behind
her, pulled her sharply, unwillingly against him. His thighs
were pressed against hers; his face was just a few inches from
her own; she could feel his breath against her skin. The scent
of his skin, of his hair—faint, male, his—came to her, and at
once, in a second, before she had time to fight it down, it
flooded through her as it always did, an overpowering want,
sharp as a voice in her veins.

'I can make you agree, Laura.' He smiled at her, coldly, and
she saw in his eyes something which she recognised and
dreaded because it matched so exactly the message in her own
body, a clouding and a fixity, the purposefulness of desire.
'Easily,' he said. 'If need be.'

'No!'

'Because I left something out, didn't I?' He forced her face
around, so she could not turn from him. 'Because it's not
quite so easy, so amicable, as I said. Is it? There's one other
factor.' He laughed softly. 'One I forbore to mention. You
want me, Laura, and I want you. And the fact that you've
been acting like a nun this last week doesn't fool me. I *know*.

You can't hide it, not from me. I *know*.' As if with a deliberate brutality, he pulled her even tighter against him, so she felt through her thin dress the hardening of his body. 'I know because I feel exactly the same thing.'

'Lust delayed?' With one last effort of will she forced a taunt into her voice. It was a mistake, and she knew it before the words were out. Robert's eyes darkened.

'That's easily taken care of,' he said, and kissed her.

It happened quickly after that, blindly, and in silence, although her mind heard a tumult of words, none of which was spoken. Afterwards she could remember only the touching, his touch against her skin, her touch against his body, so alive, so quick in her hands. The memory just of touch was so strong it arced through her body in one full sharp pulse, born again even in recollection. His mouth against hers, struggling even then, hopelessly, to turn away. His hands on her skin, touching one place, fiercely, then tenderly, and seeming to touch, such was his power, all of her body at once; her thighs, when he kissed her mouth; her breasts when he encircled her waist and lifted her to him. They stood; they lay together. They did not remove their clothes; probably it did not take very long. She felt his weight, a sharp pain, and then after, when he cried out, and she was silent, a great stillness.

Then she wept, making no sound, and very gently, carefully, Robert kissed the tears from her face. Very slowly then he undressed her, easing the silk dress over her shoulders, pushing her gently back against the rug so she lay under him, naked. She moved her hands, even then, instinctively, and very gently he lifted them aside.

'No need,' he said. 'Not now, my darling.'

The word gave her a new fierce courage; it rose up, suddenly strong within her. She opened her eyes, and looked at him, pain mixed with want clouding her vision, and yet seeing him, she felt, with a clarity she had never known before. She helped him then, with his clothes, letting her hands touch his bare skin, feeling the hard strength of his muscles, the long curving plane of his back. With a little cry of shock and pleasure she felt his skin against her own, the strange movements of his body against hers. He put his lips to her breast; she felt her nipple harden against the touch of his mouth; with one long shudder she arched her body up to him. She wanted to cry out then, some endearment. *My love*, she thought, and let her body speak for her.

'Wait,' he said, holding her, pulling her to some edge.

There was no pain now, only fluidity, ease, acceleration. He tensed.

'Laura,' he said, and took her over.

After that, when she clung to him, and he to her, when he wrapped her and held her tight in his arms until the tremors of her body subsided, and he too grew still, she knew that he had been right. Choosing this strategy, the contest was over.

She drew back a little from him, opening her eyes. He was looking at her, and the tenderness, the gentleness of his regard, destroyed the last of her defences, because, even then, it surprised her.

'You've overruled me,' she said wryly, a little sadly, foreseeing, just for a second even then, the pain that must come after.

'You will marry me,' he said. It was no longer even a question.

CHAPTER ELEVEN

IN the morning, after breakfast, Robert took her aside.

'Laura?' He locked his arms gently around her waist, and tilted her face up to him. 'My dear.' He kissed her forehead. He looked amazingly happy, calm, she thought, envying him.

'Look at me.'

Their eyes met, and instantly she felt some of her fearfulness subside. Her eyes widened, her lips parted; he bent his head and kissed her, and instantly the heavy drugged swell of pleasure, sharpened now by knowledge, beat through her body. His breath caught; he stirred. Then, gently but firmly, he held her away from him. She stared at him, seeing him with new eyes, as infinitely mysterious to her, the lover of the night before, and this man, dark, formally suited, still something of a stranger to her. She drew back; the duality aroused her, and frightened her.

'Laura.' He took her hand anxiously, his eyes searching her face. 'You're not unhappy? I haven't made you unhappy?'

'No.'

'Or angry?'

'No.'

'I hurt you?'

She hesitated, and he laughed softly, drawing her gently to him.

'Oh, Laura,' he said, 'don't deny it. You can't lie to me—not now.'

'A little, then,' she said, hoping he would never know how much.

'Listen to me.' He held her hands tight. 'I'm going to go to London today. No—just for a few hours. I'll be back this afternoon if I leave now.' He paused, the corners of his mouth lifting in a smile. 'I have to see my solicitor. One or two other things—make a will, see the registrar . . .'

'A will? The registrar?'

'But certainly. I'm going to be a married man. I have responsibilities now.' His eyes mocked her.

'You meant that, then?'

'But of course. I always mean what I say. Almost always,' he corrected himself, and she felt instantly a stab of pain. His eyes darkened. 'I shan't let you go, Laura, not now. And . . .' he lifted his hand to her lips, 'no "buts"—not any more.'

In spite of herself Laura felt something lift within her, a sense of optimism, of hope. It fired her so suddenly, so intensely, that she almost forgot her caution.

'Robert . . .' she began.

'Yes?' He had turned away to the door, but instantly he turned back.

She hesitated, then looked away to the window. 'I just wish you wouldn't go,' she said, though that was not what she had meant to say at all. 'Not now. It's such a long way. And the weather's not good. It's foggy and . . .'

He laughed, though she thought she saw an odd disappointment in his face.

'It's a hundred odd miles,' he said. 'Motorway all the way, nearly. An hour and a half each way at the most. And the fog will lift. It's nothing. It's often like this at this time of year. I'll be back before tea-time. We'll have dinner together, shall we, the way we did when you first came here? By the fire, on cushions, just the two of us? You can make me rice pudding,' he added, his eyes glinting with amusement, and he caught her to him in an impulsive hug. 'Say yes, Laura! We can talk and make plans and . . .' his arms tightened around her, 'make love.' She coloured instantly, as he had known she would, and with a quick laugh he turned to the door.

'I wanted us to do that the very first evening,' he said. 'Didn't you know?'

And then he was gone.

Laura watched the yellow fog lights of the silver Mercedes disappear into the thin morning mist that hung over the park. Then she turned quickly back into the house, her hair and her skin already cold and damp. Her body ached a little; her eyes hurt from lack of sleep; yet she did not feel tired. A weird, mad happiness had taken possession of her at his last words, and she was powerless to suppress it. It charged her with energy; suddenly she felt as if she must be active, must do something, must harness this vigour. If she sat still, if she thought, if she allowed herself to remember too much, she knew what would happen. She would think of Lydia, and the fears would start up again.

I shall marry him, she thought. *I love him. Nothing else matters.*

On an impulse she went out to the kitchen where Alex and Mrs Bowles were busy making pastry, or rather, Mrs Bowles was making it, and Alex was kneading and rolling it with an extremely heavy hand.

'Look, Laura,' he said proudly, pointing to a line of ragged round shapes in front of him, all grimy and distinctly grey. 'Cakes.'

'Vol-au-vents,' Mrs Bowles corrected, with a wink at Laura. 'Them's vol-au-vents, Master Alex.'

'Terrific!' She smiled at them both. Alex patted the last circle into place, wiped flour all over his sleeves, and trotted over to her.

'You know what I feel like doing this morning?' Laura looked at them both.

'What, Laura?'

'Spring-cleaning. I'm in just the mood.'

'Spring-cleaning?' Mrs Bowles looked doubtful for a moment, then she grinned. 'Well, it isn't the weather for it, not today anyhow. But you might be right. This house could do with a good going over—I said as much to Harry last night. I would have done it before, but it was such a rush, you all coming back from America like that, out of the blue . . .'

'Oh, Mrs Bowles, I didn't mean it was dirty.' Laura was contrite. 'It's as clean as a new pin. It's just that I thought— oh, I don't know. Flowers and things.'

Mrs Bowles chuckled. 'Flowers? Well, maybe. But a bit of elbow grease first wouldn't do no harm neither. You serious, young lady?'

'Certainly.' Laura grinned at her.

'Right, then. And don't you go sloping off neither, Master Alex. There's that chimney in the drawing room not done yet, and that's man's work. And there's that darned clock outside needing fixing. You can help Harry, you can.'

Alex, of course, was in the seventh heaven. While Laura and Mrs Bowles swept and cleaned and Hoovered and polished, he disappeared into the drawing room, clutching Harry's hands, trailing brushes and sheets. He emerged half an hour later, face and hands black with soot.

'There was a nest!' he announced excitedly. 'A great big one—a jackdaw's. It fell down whoosh, just like that, and it just missed me!'

'It doesn't look as if it missed,' said Laura, with mock sternness. 'It looks as if it was bang on target. Into the bath with you!'

'But Laura!' There was a wail of protest. 'It's the middle of the day!'

'I don't care if it's the middle of the night. Into the bath!'

They worked on until the early afternoon, pausing only for a picnic lunch at the kitchen table, when Alex was mesmerised by Harry Bowles' ability to consume nearly half a pound of cheese and ten pickled onions.

'Ten!' he whispered to Laura afterwards. 'Think of that! Will I be able to do that one day, d'you think, Laura?'

'Of course you will, twenty maybe. Wait and see.'

She hugged him, and looked around her happily.

The house had been transformed by their efforts. It looked now as she had imagined it might look, that first day. The eighteenth-century furniture smelled of beeswax; the silver shone. Mrs Bowles had brought out the summer covers for the drawing room chairs and sofas; Harry had hung the summer curtains. The room now looked light and welcoming. Logs were stacked, ready to be lit, in the great fireplace. Laura had placed flowers on the tables: bowls of iris and tulips and narcissus. Their scent came to her on the air and her spirits lifted. Now they need not use the morning room so much, she thought happily. She was lucky, she told herself; lucky, lucky, lucky. This beautiful house, filled with so many beautiful rooms, with such a powerful sense of Robert

Wentworth's ancestors, would be her home. Their home. She
had been stupid to think so much of Lydia, she thought,
standing in the long gallery, looking at the lines of portraits.
Wentworths had fought with Drake's Armada, with the
Royalists against the Cromwellians; the young men of the
family had died—foolishly and wastefully, Robert had once
said—defending the frontiers of Victoria's Empire. These stiff
men in their ruffs; these Gainsborough women in their silks,
holding their greyhounds on leash in the park, they had lived
and moved and had their being in this house. How foolish to
imagine, as she had done, that Lydia's spirit dominated the
house. How could one woman dominate a place where one
family had lived for more than four hundred years?

With Alex she went outside and stood by the entrance,
looking down the drive. The mist still had not quite lifted, but
the sun had come out, its rays piercing the cloud cover with a
gentle diffused light. Mrs Bowles came out to join them,
flicking her duster. She gestured back into the house.

'Looks lovely, it does, now. Like the old days. When old
Mrs Wentworth was alive.' She sighed. 'My Harry got that
clock going again, even—did you notice? Said it was all rusted
up at the back, he had quite a job with it. Mind, it hasn't gone
now for near on eight years, so it's no wonder.'

'Eight years?' Laura turned to her, staring.

'At least, bless you. Chimes the hour lovely, it does. I can
hear it in my kitchen.'

She left them then, and Laura turned with a quick
movement to look up at the faded blue face above her.
Tempus fugit. Quickly she looked down at her watch, then
back at the clock. They synchronised; it was two-thirty. Her
heart lifted: so she had imagined that; it was coincidence
merely, nothing to do with Lydia at all. She laughed
suddenly.

'The sun's coming out. It's going to clear. Come on, Alex.
Let's walk down to the village. I want to go to the grocer's,
and a walk would do us good, don't you think?'

They pulled on coats and boots, then set off down the
drive, Alex darting ahead of her, then running back, then
darting off again in a sudden explosion of high spirits that
matched her own. By the time they returned, she thought
happily, it would be time for Robert to get back.

She bought a few things in the grocer's—Lapsang
Souchong tea, because she knew he liked it, a honeycomb, for

Alex. While she shopped, he poked about in the large old-
fashioned shop, and peered out of the window, watching the
street. Though Laura bought little, it was slow, the delays
made her impatient. Everything was weighed and measured
on huge shiny brass scales, and tipped into small green paper
sacks.

'Oh, and some rice. The round Italian kind . . .'

The old man who owned the shop fumbled around on the
shelves.

'Don't get much call for that, we don't . . . now where is it?'
He straightened up triumphantly. 'A pound, did you say?'

Laura nodded.

'Going to a wedding, are you?' He looked at her keenly.
'Wedding rice, this is. Always threw it, we did, when I was a
boy. None of that confetti stuff then.'

He handed her the packet, and Laura paid, her face scarlet.
He had recognised her, she was sure of it, from her days at the
Fieldings'. Everyone in the village would know she now
worked at Marston. As she left the shop with Alex she saw
the man turn to his wife, say something, nod after her. She
could imagine the village gossip, only too well, when the news
got out. *Him still grieving after his brother's wife, something
unnatural. Still, the little boy needed a mother. They say . . .*
She tossed back her hair, putting such thoughts from her.
What did she care for village gossip?

They turned down the village street, towards the green. Laura
took Alex's hand, holding it tightly. He had gone very quiet, she
thought; perhaps he was bored. Suddenly he stopped.

'I saw Mummy today, Laura.'

Alex was swinging one foot back and forth, kicking the worn
grass with the toe of his wellingtons. His tone was perfectly
ordinary. Laura stopped abruptly.

'You can't have done that, Alex,' she said gently.

'I did. When you was in that shop.' He hesitated. 'She drove
past in a big red car. Then she stopped, and I saw her.'

Laura stared straight ahead of her; she could not bring
herself to look at him. Across the green the branches of a fir
tree lifted, shifted in the breeze. Carefully she drew in her
breath, steadying herself.

'It can't have been Mummy, Alex. You must have made a
mistake,' she said, keeping her voice gentle, even. 'You do
understand that, don't you, darling?'

'Yes.' He kicked the grass in front of him. 'Mummy's dead.

Uncle Robert told me.' He hesitated. 'I liked Mummy—when she was there.'

'Of course you did, darling.' Affection suddenly fierce in her heart, she turned to him, bending down so their faces were level. 'And she loved you, Alex. I'm sure of it, even though I never knew her. And you'll always remember that, won't you?'

'I think so.' He looked at her doubtfully, his eyes wide in his face, and extraordinarily dark. His foot had stopped swinging. 'She didn't love my daddy, though.'

'I'm sure that's not true, Alex,' Laura started, but he cut her off.

'Yes, it is. She said so—in the car in America. She said she hadn't never loved him. And she threw her special ring out the window—the one Daddy gave her.'

'Alex,' gently Laura took his two small hands in hers, 'why do you think she said that?'

'I don't know.' He paused. 'She was taking us to see an Indian lady—a magic one; she told me. She asked Uncle Robert to go, and he wouldn't. My daddy didn't want to go either, he said she was driving too fast, and Mummy got very cross, and ... then I don't remember.' His lip trembled; Laura tightened her grip on his hands.

'But there you are,' she said. 'Don't you see, Alex? She was angry.' She hesitated; his eyes never left her face. 'You know how grown-ups get angry sometimes? They get so angry they feel they could burst and then ... then they say things they don't really mean at all. And afterwards they feel sorry.' She smiled at him gently. 'Haven't you ever done that, Alex? I have, lots of times.'

He hesitated. 'I was angry with Uncle Robert once,' he said. 'When he wouldn't let me ride the big pony. Years and years and years ago.'

'And what did you do, Alex, when you were angry with Uncle Robert?'

'I stamped my foot.' A little ghost of a smile came to his lips. 'And I said he was horrid and I didn't never want to play with him again.'

'And was that true, Alex?'

He shook his head wordlessly, and Laura put her arms around him.

'You see?' She held him tight. 'When we're angry we say things we don't mean at all. We try to hurt people. It's very wrong, but we do it.'

'You mean Mummy didn't mean what she said?' He looked at her solemnly.

'I'm sure she can't have done, aren't you?' She paused, offering up a silent inchoate prayer that what she said was the truth. 'You see, Alex, grown-ups sometimes make loving someone a very difficult business. And they don't need to at all. It's really very simple. You'll understand when you're older.'

'I love you, Laura.' He bestowed a rather perfunctory kiss on her cheek. 'Lots. Shall we go home now?'

And, with every appearance of unconcern, as if all his doubts and worries had gone, he suddenly twisted up and out of her arms and ran across the grass. Laura watched him, pain and love for him wrenching at her heart. Then, gathering up her packages, she followed after him.

'Come on, Alex,' she said, catching his hand. 'Let's hurry.'

'Will Uncle Robert be back?'

'I hope so, Alex,' she said. 'Oh, I hope so!'

And together they began to run.

They hurried back into the village, then out on to the road to Marston. In the High Street all the shops had their lights on, though it was not yet four. But then, the mist was thicker now, heavier than she had realised, lying in patches so, as they walked along the side of the narrow road, it sometimes enveloped them and then, for a few yards, cleared.

'Keep in to the verge, Alex.' She held his hand. 'It's narrow here. Look, walk just by the ditch. Come on, it's not far now.'

'I like it.' Alex sniffed the damp air happily. 'It's an adventure, Laura. Do you think we'll get lost?'

Laura grinned. All they had to do, she thought, was keep on for about half a mile and then turn into the drive. Even in a pea-souper it would be hard to miss the way.

'You never know, Alex,' she said. 'You'd better keep your eyes open.'

They walked on for a little way in silence.

'She was very pretty, the lady in the red car,' Alex said at last. 'I didn't really think it was Mummy.' He paused. 'It was a big car, a French car, like the toy one Uncle Robert bought me at the airport.'

'A Citroën?'

'That's right. A red . . . one of those.'

Laura's footsteps faltered for a moment. A red Citroën. Only one person in the village drove such a car; Zara. She paused for a second, frowning; then walked on. She had never thought of it, but it was true, there was a resemblance between Zara and the picture she had seen of Lydia. The fair hair, cut so short; the slim, boyish, athletic figure. How odd, she thought; I never realised it before. But the thought drifted out of her mind almost as quickly as it came; she increased her pace a little. She thought of Robert Wentworth. She would tell him, she thought, what she felt. It was, after all, quite simple. And much too important to lie.

'Can we have toast for tea, Laura?'

She smiled. 'Yes. And honey. I bought you a honeycomb, Alex—a whole one. It's beautiful.'

They had passed the Fieldings' house now. Laura did not turn her head to see it. They were nearly there, she thought, remembering how she had come along this same road all those weeks before. They were coming to the wood now, and just a little way on, on the left, was the turning into the drive. She peered at the hedges; they had hit another patch of mist. It would be infuriating to miss it.

Cloud swirled around them. She hitched her coat higher around her throat, and paused to knot Alex's scarf. It was a little eerie, she thought, as the strands of white cloud eddied around them.

'Isn't it odd, Alex,' she said. 'So quiet. The mist muffles the sound, like snow.'

'I don't like it much.' Suddenly he gripped her hand. The wood was on their right now.

'Don't worry,' she said. 'Marston is on high ground. When we go up the drive we'll come out of it.'

They had gone another fifty yards when they heard the voices, muffled at first. Then the footsteps. Laura strained her eyes ahead of them, suddenly perturbed. Had they come too far? Could they have missed the turning?

Then, as they rounded the bend, they saw them, the mist suddenly lifting a little. Marie Christine, pushing the pram, Samantha and Jessy clutching its handle, walking along on the wrong side of the road, their backs to the oncoming traffic. They saw each other in the same instant. Marie Christine came to an abrupt halt, peering through the mist, Samantha and Jessy following her gaze. There was a moment's silence, then Marie Christine gave a sharp exclamation.

'*Mais c'est incroyable!* Laura!'

She broke into an odd absurd little run, the pram bumping

on the grass verge, missing the ditch by inches. She lifted her hand and waved.

'Laura! Laura! *C'est moi!*'

Her voice echoed across the misty road; Laura increased her pace.

'Marie Christine—hang on! Be careful! You're on the wrong side of the road. Wait!'

She lifted her face, smiling. Samantha and Jessy had seen her now. They paused, then broke into a run. Jessy gave a little cry of welcome; she was wearing a red woollen cap, with a knitted bobble that jiggled up and down as she ran forward.

'Sammy, it's Laura. Look, it's Laura!'

Then Laura saw the car. It made no sound almost, just a low hissing from its tyres on the wet road. Its lights were on full, suddenly huge and yellow, looming up out of the mist, rounding the bend. Apart from its lights, it was almost invisible, its silver bodywork ghostly in the mist. Laura froze; time slowed. Jessy had not seen it. She had let go her sister's hand and was darting forward, her face suddenly clear in the mist, eager with excitement, her breath coming in tiny white puffs in the cold air.

'*Mon dieu!*' Marie Christine had realised the danger in the same second. She stopped, as if incapable of movement, her mouth a round dark O of horror. '*Non!* Jessy . . .'

It seemed to Laura that she herself moved very slowly, as if her limbs were lead. First she pushed Alex aside, roughly, into the safety of the hedge. Then she moved forward, into the road, into the headbeams, seeing her arms lift in front of her in slow motion, illumined, gold . . .

Jessy slowed. There was just time. As she saw the sudden panic register in the child's eyes, her run halt in fatal indecision, Laura reached her. She pushed her, hard, full in the chest, so the child reeled backwards with a sudden sharp cry of terror. Then as Laura had known it must, the car caught her own body, even as it braked. It tossed her up, high, amazingly high, up over the yellow lamps, then down, spinning, across the wide hard expanse of silver metal. She still held her packages; one hit the metal and burst. Tiny crystals of rice, skeetering over the silver bonnet.

She could hear, through mist, Alex and his father, both screaming her name.

Voices. She heard voices.

Twenty, if that. The visibility was appalling. I hurried because I was late. But I slowed at the bend . . . Oh God!

Blankets. Yes, a rug.

J'ai téléphoné. Il viendra tout de suite . . .

The surgery's five minutes from here. Goddammit, how can it take so long?

Perhaps you shouldn't have moved her. They say . . .

Her pulse is quite strong.

Fingers around her wrist, pressed to the side of her throat. *Laura.*

Then a shuffling; silence.

Hands against the side of her head, cool, impersonal. Feeling her skull, turning her head, first this way, then that. Lifting each arm, each leg. Cool firm pressure against her ribs. First the right side, then the left. Pain like an explosion of light.

Laura. A snapping noise. *Laura. Open your eyes!*

She lifted her lids. Closed them again.

Good girl. Once more—that's it!

A pencil of light, burning into her eyes. She blinked.

I'm cold.

You're very lucky, young woman.

Rugs.

Where's Robert?

With the doctor, madam.

Then you fetch some tea.

She opened her eyes, then closed them again, then opened them. The room was blurred with light, fuzzy at the edges; it moved, shifted, steadied, resolved itself into a pattern. Furniture, lamps.

Lamplight on fair hair. Blue eyes.

She lifted her hand. It took an age to reach her temple. Her head ached.

'Lydia?' She reached for the face. 'Don't cry. Alex is safe.'

The mouth moved jaggedly in the face. 'You're in shock, Laura. Don't you know me?'

The room, the face, came into focus. She struggled to sit up. 'Where am I?'

'At my house. They brought you here.'

'Zara!'

She nodded, sighed, straightened up and turned away. Laura watched her as she felt her consciousness return. Slowly, like waking from a deep exhausted sleep, she felt her memory begin to seep back.

'It was Robert's Mercedes?'

'Yes.'

Zara reached for a cigarette, lit it, her hands shaking a little, the smooth cap of gold hair bent in concentration towards the flame of the lighter. She was standing in the middle of a small round rug, perhaps five feet away. The two women looked at each other.

'You saved Jessy's life.'

'Please . . . as long as she's all right . . .'

'Thank you.'

Zara drew deeply on her cigarette, inhaled, blew out the smoke. It seemed to steady her.

'It's funny,' she said meditatively. 'I used to hate you. I shall probably hate you again tomorrow. But just at this moment, I don't.'

'Zara . . .'

'No, don't interrupt. We haven't long, and we might as well be truthful. Besides, it's easier, isn't it, at a moment like this?'

She gave a little hard laugh; instantly it brought back to Laura memories of the months she had spent in this house. It sharpened, defined, the woman in front of her. She looked at her tiredly, still a little blinded by the pain which now built in her body. How odd, she thought, a little lightheadedly, that she should have made that confusion. There was a similarity, as Alex had seen, but Zara was not really like Lydia, not close up. She felt her eyelids droop; pain knotted in her side.

'You're not hurt. The doctor came—there's nothing broken, just bruising. You were lucky.'

Zara was watching her intently, her eyes glittering, catlike.

'Lucky?' Laura stared at her, something in Zara's eyes making her tired consciousness alert.

With a sudden impatient gesture Zara turned away. She sat down opposite Laura, crossing her long slender legs silkily, picking up from the table beside her a small ivory box. She played with it idly, flipping and closing the lid. The minutes lengthened; from across the hall Laura could hear the sound of voices; she rested her head tiredly against the back of her chair, wishing someone would come.

'Michael and I are divorcing. You know that, presumably?' Zara spoke abruptly, out of the silence.

'Yes—I heard. I'm sorry.'

'Michael's keeping the house. The children will stay with him, Mrs Grove, Marie Christine—the whole *ménage*.' She paused. 'I'm going to South Africa, and I shan't come back. There's nothing to keep me here now.'

Their eyes met; there was a silence. Laura struggled to focus on what was being said to her. She couldn't understand why they were having this conversation at all—unless Zara was in shock too. She looked at her, fighting down the waves of pain that blurred her vision. If she were in shock there was no sign of it. She appeared now totally in control, as if she were waiting for something.

'Please, Zara,' she said, 'I don't know why you're telling me all this.'

'A man might have kept me here.' Zara had not even paused. 'The right man: a good man. I like good men, oddly enough. I find them attractive. A challenge. Yes, a strong man. A good man. Robert, for instance.'

Laura's head jerked forward, and Zara laughed softly.

'Does that make you jealous? It needn't. Not of me.'

There was a silence. Laura fumbled with the rugs that wrapped her, forcing down the pain that ebbed and flowed through her body, dulling her mind. Her hands gripped the arms of her chair; with difficulty, for her legs hardly held her, she stood up. She swayed, straightened.

'I'm going to marry Robert,' she said.

Not a muscle moved in Zara's face. 'I know,' she said calmly.

The room pitched and shifted; the one still point was Zara's face.

'You knew?' Laura stared at her. 'Did Robert tell you?'

'No. Lydia did.'

The silence in the room seemed to lift, gather, batten on Laura.

'That's not possible.' Her voice shook, steadied. 'Lydia's dead. She died before I even met Robert. She couldn't have . . .'

Zara uncoiled herself from the chair and stood up in one graceful movement.

'*She walks in beauty like the night,*' she said softly, her voice taking on an odd chanting tone. '*And all that's best of dark and bright, Meet in her aspect and her eyes . . .*' She laughed softly, and Laura felt her blood go cold. 'You know the poem? Not one of Byron's better efforts, but Lydia was obsessed with it. She was obsessed with all sorts of things, in fact—a very stupid woman. Nervous, fanciful, always consulting people—astrologers, Tarot readers, clairvoyants, aura-readers—charlatans.' She paused. 'Reading substance into dreams. I have no patience with that kind of thing myself. But then she was very much in love with Robert, and she was rich, and she really had very little else to do.'

She paused, standing close to Laura now, and suddenly Laura had again her old sense of Zara's curious destructive magnetism. It held her now, that malevolence, as she had seen it hold others. She could not speak. Lifting her hand, Zara flicked Laura's black hair with the tips of her long scarlet-painted nails. One little touch.

'Dark and bright,' she said mockingly, looking into Laura's eyes. 'He speaks of raven tresses too. The poem is full of such lapses. Not that Lydia minded—she relished them. She was always a masochist. Slightly hysterical, perhaps. Not like you at all. She was convinced, you see, that Robert would marry eventually—a woman with black hair, like yours. She described you to me, many times. She saw you in her dreams, sensed you at Marston. It was why she hated to go there. You haunted her, Laura.'

'No . . .'

'I'm afraid so.' Zara laughed softly. 'It hadn't occurred to you, perhaps, that people could be haunted by the future, as well as the past?' She paused. 'And then there was Alex, of course. After Alex was born it all got *much* worse. He didn't look like her, you see, not in the least. There was nothing of his mother in him. He looked like his father, but also like you. That accelerated things rather—the hysteria, the imaginings. It was why she insisted on going out to New Mexico, I think. Maybe she thought she'd be free of you there . . .'

'Stop this! Leave me alone!' With a sharp gesture, Laura put her hand up in front of her face, turned her head away. 'It's not true! I don't believe any of it . . .'

'Neither did I.' Zara stepped back a pace. Slowly she looked Laura up and down, and unwillingly, reluctantly, Laura met her gaze. 'I thought she was imagining the whole thing. Talking about her Scottish ancestors, her second sight—it was pathetic. I envisaged a different scenario as far as Robert was concerned. Quite different. But then I was wrong and she was right. I'd never have hired you, of course, if I'd listened to her. But I did. Remiss of me not to notice I'd given myself an adversary.'

'I never thought of you as an adversary,' Laura said slowly.

'How about a rival?' Zara's voice rose in a taunt.

'Not that either.'

Zara's mouth tightened; two spots of colour started to her cheeks.

'And Lydia?'

'I *was* afraid of Lydia.' Laura paused, gazing into Zara's eyes, held by them. Then she looked away abruptly, shifting her gaze with difficulty, like an animal before a snake. And as she broke the gaze, her mind cleared. She felt something within her, something stored and powerful, gather strength. She waited, then she spoke. 'I'm not afraid of her any more.'

'Well, well,' Zara said. 'And you were never afraid of me?'

'No, I wasn't,' Laura said quietly. 'Should I have been?'

The two women faced each other; the room was silent, still.

'Should I have been?' She repeated her question into the silence, like a challenge, and it was Zara's gaze which faltered first.

'Perhaps.' She shrugged, and then laughed, her tone dismissive, suddenly brisk. She lifted her hand. 'That medallion you're wearing,' she said. 'What is it? A good luck charm?'

'So I was told. Someone gave it to me, in New Mexico.' Laura paused. Then on a shaft of instinct, a primitive voice in her mind as direct as a command, she reached up her hands to her throat and undid its clasp, her gaze never leaving Zara's face.

'I don't think I need it now. Do you?'

She held the smooth metal in her hand for a second, and then lightly, casually, dropped it on to the polished surface of the small table beside her. As it fell, Zara turned abruptly away. When she spoke again, her voice was perfectly even, quite normal.

'I'll fetch Robert for you, shall I?' she said. 'He'll want to take you home, I expect. You feel strong enough now.'

'Yes,' Laura replied, though she knew Zara did not question, simply stated.

She paused then by the door, her scarlet nails vivid against its white paint.

'Goodbye, then, Laura,' she said softly. 'I shan't see you again. I wish you well . . .' She broke off. 'No, perhaps that's overstating it a little. I don't wish you ill, not any more. Shall we put it like that?'

'Zara . . .' On a sudden impulse, Laura swung round. But

she had gone; a trace of her scent lingered in the air, sweet, slightly foetid, oil of patchouli. She had always hated it.

She stood for a little while, feeling the strength return to her limbs, looking down at the silver and torquoise medallion where it glinted in the lamplight, and thinking.

Then, shortly after, she heard voices in the hall, and Robert and Alex came in, and took her hands, and took her back to Marston.

CHAPTER TWELVE

'TWICE.'

He stood in front of the fire looking down at her, his face lit and shadowed by its flames, his eyes dark as water at night. The room was hushed; from the hall the longcase clock ticked faintly, chimed the half hour; a log in the grate shifted, sending up a spurt of greenish flame. Laura looked up at him, at the powerful body, so tall and so strong. His black jacket was unbuttoned, his shirt open at the neck, so she could see the long line of his throat, the hair that curled dark on his chest. His hands were clenched; his face troubled.

'Twice, and each time . . .' He broke off. 'I could have killed you, Laura!'

'Three times,' she said gently. 'You nearly ran me down in your car once before. Before we even met—I told you. Don't you remember?'

'Oh, God . . .' He turned away.

'It's all right.' She leaned towards him. 'Don't you see? Three times? The magic number?' She smiled. 'Anyone remotely superstitious would tell you.'

'You take it all remarkably calmly,' he cut her off angrily. 'Two—three brushes with death in such a short time, all connected with me? More than anything else in the world I want . . .' He broke off abruptly. When he spoke again his voice was more gentle. 'Laura, don't you see? I'm concerned for you—for your safety. I don't understand any of this—why these things should have happened.'

'They were just accidents.'

'Accidents?' With a sudden gesture of angry despair, he passed his hand over his face. 'It's like a nightmare. I keep thinking I'll wake up, that none of this has happened, John, Lydia, Alex—and now you!'

There was silence.

'Alex is better now. He's getting well again, healing. I'm sure of it. Not just his speaking, but everything,' said Laura.

'And you? What about you? You could have been killed tonight. It's a miracle you weren't—the doctor said so. And then the time in the pool. I thought—I don't know what I thought. But I believed you'd be safe here, with me, at Marston.'

'I am safe now.' Gently she stopped his angry exclamations. The sureness in her voice reached him, steadied him. She held his gaze across the few feet that separated them, and gradually she saw his face grow calmer. His eyes darkened; with an odd broken gesture he lifted his hand to her, and then moved swiftly, kneeling down beside her.

'Laura.' He hesitated. 'Show me . . . I want to see.'

'It's nothing, just bruising. It will go in a few days.'

'Show me.'

She bent her head, her hair falling like a dark curtain between them, and then slowly she reached for the buttons of her blouse. She undid them one by one, to the waist, her bare skin underneath gold in the firelight. When it was unfastened, Robert reached forward very gently and parted her blouse, easing it aside, over her high young breasts. She heard the sudden sharp intake of his breath; she looked down.

The bruising was all to one side, a great dark stain under her left breast, down over her ribs, over her heart.

'Oh my God, Laura!' His face crumpled. Then, very gently, with a profound tenderness, he laid his hand gently over her side, covering the mark with his palm, the lightest of touches. Then he moved, bending his head, and very gently kissed the bruised skin, her breasts, her throat. She trembled instantly, though not from pain, and lifting her face up to him, holding her chin in his hands, he looked a long while into her eyes. Then, very softly, opening her lips under his, he kissed her mouth, a long kiss, a sad one, like a leavetaking. At last he drew away from her, and very slowly, one by one, he fastened the buttons of her blouse to the neck, lifted the long dark strands of her hair for a moment, letting them slip through his fingers, and drew back. He took her two hands in his.

'My darling Laura.' He spoke with difficulty, but held her gaze steadily. 'You know what I'm going to say, don't you?

No, let me. You must.' His eyes clouded. 'It can't be, Laura. Not now. I can't take the risk. I want you—I want you here, more than I can ever say, more than you would ever believe.' He hesitated a moment. 'But I can't marry you, not now. And you can't stay here, not with me, even if you wanted to. And last night . . .' he paused, and dropped his gaze, 'I forced you. When I thought I couldn't persuade you . . . I shouldn't have done that. It was deeply wrong of me. I shall blame myself, always.' He broke off with an exclamation of pain and anger, and when she did not speak, he drew in a long shuddering breath. 'Don't you see, Laura? I had no right to do that, no right to ask you to marry me. You're young—you have your whole life ahead of you. Why should you throw it away in a loveless marriage? And besides . . .' He saw her turn her head sharply away and pressed on. 'There's *this*.' He gestured to her side. 'What that Indian woman told you—it was *true*, you can't deny that. Twice, three times. It won't happen again.' His mouth set in a hard line. 'You must go away from here, Laura—away from me, away from Alex. I'll look after you—help you. I'll give you anything you need . . . but you can't stay here. We must not meet.' He paused. 'You won't make the decision, because of Alex, I know that, so I have to make it for us—finally. And so please, Laura, dear Laura, don't make it any harder. No arguments, all right?' He smiled at her, and lightly pressed her hand against his lips.

Laura stared at him. His voice seemed to come to her from across a great distance. For a moment she felt something within her, that stored power, flicker and waver. Was he telling her the truth? Or was he just being gentle, avoiding something else out of kindness, avoiding telling her perhaps that last night, so young, so inexperienced, she had after all been a disappointment to him?

'Last night . . .' She hesitated, afraid to meet his eyes. 'I don't regret that. I shall never regret it!' She lifted her head fiercely. 'But perhaps I wasn't very good. I'm not experienced. Maybe I did all the wrong things, disappointed you.'

'Laura, *no*!' She saw incredulity in his eyes, then a warmth and tenderness so intense it lit her own heart. 'Please—you mustn't think that. Never. I . . .' He made as if to reach for her and at the last moment drew back. 'Listen,' he said gently, 'and believe me, because I would never lie to you. You're beautiful, Laura.' He touched her face lightly. 'You have a lovely face and a lovely body, and when you make love, it feels as if you do so from the heart, and no man—no man, do you hear me?—could have more happiness, more joy, than that. What's more important is that you're beautiful in other ways, more lasting ways, and more important ways. Here, and here,' he touched her head and her heart. 'And *here*. And so——' he drew back, forcing his face to be stern, though she saw a smile tug at the corners of his mouth, 'you didn't disappoint me. I think you know that, don't you? I might have disappointed you, of course. Though I think—despite your inexperience, as you put it, not altogether . . .'

'Oh . . .' Impulsively, she caught his hand and held it against her. Gently, slowly, he disengaged himself.

'Don't, Laura,' he said in a low broken voice. 'Please don't. That can't change anything, don't you see? It mustn't. I meant what I said. You must leave here.'

'I won't go!' Suddenly all the restraint burst from her. She could bear it no longer. 'I won't. I can't. I love you!'

Robert drew back from her sharply.

'Please!' Desperately she reached for him. 'Don't stop me now. Let me tell you—I must! I've wanted to for so long. It was so hard. Please, Robert, let me speak!'

He was suddenly very still, his face dark, unreadable. Again she had the sensation she had had the first time she saw him, of poise, detachment, and it almost checked her, but not quite.

'I love you,' she said, aware now of how inadequate the words were. 'I loved you almost from the first. And then it just grew and grew. When we were here—in London, in America. At first I thought I was just being stupid, I tried to pretend to myself.' She paused. 'I knew when you were near me—I wanted you so much, you see. I'd never felt anything so strong in my life. And then—then I knew it wasn't just that. You're good and kind and funny and strong and—I loved you. It made me so happy. I wanted to tell you and . . .'

'But you didn't.' He cut her off, his voice suddenly harsh. 'I asked you, that night by the pool, and you denied it.'

'I was lying! I was so afraid, you see. I didn't want you to know . . .'

'Afraid?'

'I thought you'd send me away! Don't you see? I'd heard what you'd said. I knew what you'd do if you thought I loved you. You wouldn't want to hurt me. And so you'd send me away, just as you're doing now.' She stopped abruptly. 'I knew, you see, that you didn't love me, that you couldn't, ever. But it didn't matter.' She hesitated shyly, and smiled at him. 'Well, perhaps it did matter, a little. It hurt, of course. It still does. But it's not the most important thing. The most important thing is that I love you and I always shall. And I want to be with you. Please, can you understand that? Believe me, there's no false hopes any more. I wouldn't burden you with my feelings. It's just that I can't bear it any longer—pretending, lying, when I want you to know the truth.'

'Laura.' He leaned forward and took her two hands in his, his face suddenly grave. 'Tell me, why did you think that about me? Was it just because of what you heard me say—that night on the terrace?'

She sighed. 'That was the confirmation, I suppose. But I knew, you see, long before that. Before we even went to America.'

'Knew *what*?' His voice was tinged with angry exasperation. She met his eyes.

'I knew about Lydia,' she said simply. 'Zara told me. The first day you brought me here, when she came—don't you remember? So I knew you loved Lydia and she loved you. I knew she was the only woman for you, that you would always love her.' She paused. 'And I knew about Alex. I knew he was your child.'

'*What?*' He drew back from her roughly, his face suddenly so dark with anger that it terrified her.

'Please,' she said pleadingly. 'It didn't make any difference, believe me. It made me love Alex more. And I didn't—well, *judge* you and Lydia. How could I? I felt the same thing you must feel—so strongly. I could understand—a little. Truly I could.'

'God damn it!' He swore violently, so she recoiled from him. 'Zara told you all this?'

Laura stared at him in confusion. 'Yes—but it wasn't just that. I could see it in your face. When you talked about Lydia, when you thought of her. When you looked at me sometimes, I knew you were remembering her. Zara said, you see, even then, right at the beginning, if you kissed anybody, touched them . . .'

'What?'

'That you'd be thinking of Lydia.'

'And you thought *that*?' Robert stared at her, his eyes blazing with anger in his pale face. 'When you were in my arms, when I . . . last night?'

She looked away. 'No,' she said softly, 'I didn't. But I suppose that was because I couldn't bear to believe it was true.'

'It *wasn't* true. None of it! Damn it, Laura, look me in the eyes. Are you blind? You must be mad! How can you have believed that?'

Slowly she turned her head to face him once more; the firelight flickered against the hard planes of his face, and the truth in his eyes was of such force it seemed to burn her mind with its brightness. *Dark and bright*, she thought, confused suddenly by the conflict of pain and hope in her heart.

Robert sighed, and his grip on her hands tightened.

'Laura, listen to me.' His face grew calmer. 'You will believe me—you must! I should have told you all this before—explained. If I'd suspected for one moment what you thought, what you felt——' He broke off. 'So—listen now and listen well, because I want there to be no more confusions.' Even then his eyes darkened as if in pain. 'Lydia—we'll begin with Lydia. I never loved her—never! And Alex is not my child. He's John's child. It's impossible that he could be mine, because I never touched Lydia, never kissed her, never had any contact with her whatsoever other than as a friend, my brother's wife. And never wanted to. Do you understand?'

She nodded silently. He hesitated.

'It was a long time,' he said finally, 'several years after her marriage in fact, before I began to realise what Lydia felt for me. Perhaps I was a little blind, I don't know. But because I never thought of her in that way it simply never occurred to me that she felt anything for me. I rarely saw her, in any case. I was always away working. If I came here it was usually just with John; she was so often in London. When we did meet, I didn't particularly like her. She was odd, a little fey, affected about that. And cold. But John loved her—passionately, almost from the first day he set eyes on her. Intemperate, that——' he glanced down at her, his voice dry, and the candour of his look made her heart start to race. 'Perhaps it runs in the family. Though I have a good deal more judgment in these matters than my brother.'

He paused, then his face grew serious again.

'Then, about eight years ago, when I was here one summer, she told me. She was rather melodramatic about the whole thing, as I recall. Forbidden love, all that. I think the idea of

its being forbidden was the chief attraction for her ...
Anyway, I tried to humour her out of it, told her it was
absurd, that she was imagining all these feelings. And I made
it clear, quite clear, that the love she thought she felt for me
was not returned, and never would be. Then I left.'

He looked down, then, at his hands, and Laura saw them
clench on his lap.

'After that, it got worse. She began to write to me. Once she
turned up at my London house, another time on the set of
some film. She thought I was sending messages to her,
telepathically. She began to have dreams ...' He hesitated.
'She became obsessed that I would marry. She said she even
knew what my future wife would look like. She found some
poem of Byron's, which she claimed described this woman.'

'*Dark and bright*,' Laura quoted softly. 'I know—I saw the
book, last night. And today, after the accident, Zara told me.'

His face darkened. 'She told you that, then?'

'It didn't matter. It made no difference. Not then. I think
she knew that.'

'She's evil. I detest her!' He spoke violently. 'I always
thought she was partly to blame for all this—for Lydia. They
were friends of sorts. Lydia trusted her, and Zara encouraged
her—told her she had second sight, took her off to see palm-
readers, clairvoyants, in London. And then no doubt laughed
behind her back.'

'Poor Lydia,' Laura said softly.

'It was sad.' His mouth tightened. 'And not just for her, for
John, too. You see—Alex was born. I hoped then that she'd
be cured, that all these fantasies she'd woven around herself
would fade away. But they didn't. After the birth she was ill;
she had a breakdown. When she recovered, she told John.
Except she altered the story. She told him we were in love,
that Alex was my son. I think, by then, she almost believed it.'
He paused. 'It was terrible. I loved him so much, you see,
we'd always been so close, right from when we were children.
I came down here to see him and there was a dreadful scene.
Even now I hate to think of it. You see, no matter what I
said, no matter what I did, there was always that doubt,
lingering. Every time he looked at Alex ...' His voice almost
broke, and Laura reached quickly for his hand.

'He must have realised,' she said urgently. 'I'm sure.
Knowing you as he did, loving you, I don't believe he can
have gone on doubting you.'

'Perhaps. I hope so.' His voice was grim. 'Anyway, I did the only thing I could do—I stayed away. When Lydia was here I never came to Marston. I didn't see her, communicate with her, in any way, for four years. Not once. And then they came out to America.'

'But why?' She stared at him. 'Why then, after all that time?'

'John thought she was over it. He insisted. I tried to dissuade him and he wouldn't listen. He said Lydia was cured, that he'd know she was when we were all able to meet again, normally, like a family. He wouldn't listen to me. They came. And—well, you know the rest.'

'She got worse?'

'Immediately. She'd always had headaches, migraines. They started up again, she had to see a doctor out there. And then she found that damned Indian woman, the one you saw.'

There was a silence. Laura took his hand.

'What did she tell her?'

He met her eyes. 'She told her about *you*.'

'Oh, God!'

'You see now why I wouldn't tell you? Couldn't?' He hesitated. 'When it happened, I didn't believe it. I dismissed it, tried to get her to put it out of her mind. But it was vivid, she said, like an hallucination. The woman didn't speak. Lydia just saw you.'

'Like a photograph?' She leaned towards him. 'A slide—when it's slotted into a projector, and you see the image, quite suddenly?'

'That's right.' He looked at her grimly. 'You felt the same thing?'

'Yes, I did,' She paused. 'I saw you.'

He stared at her for a long moment, in silence, then made a quick impatient gesture.

'All this can't be true. It's not possible. There's no rational explanation for it.'

'I'm sure there is.' She touched his hand gently. 'People always find terms, don't they? Old-fashioned ones, like fate, second sight. Modern ones—auto-suggestion, pre-cognition. I expect there's someone somewhere who could explain it all very neatly, rationally, and still miss the point. It doesn't matter.' She paused. 'Finish the story.'

'You're very confident suddenly.' Robert shot her a

sideways glance. 'You sound like a sybil. Any more of that and I'll . . . You sound appallingly smug, do you know that?'

'I'm sorry,' she said gently. 'But you should go on. Now.'

He hesitated, his face growing dark again, his mouth bitter.

'Then——' He paused. 'What happened then is the worst of all, for me. You see, Lydia was determined to go back to the Indian woman. Nothing I said could dissuade her. She insisted, she pleaded—and she begged me to go with her. I agreed.'

'You *agreed*?' Laura stared at him.

'Yes, I did,' he said bitterly. 'I thought it was impossible to prevent her from going. That it might help, perhaps, if I did go. I thought I might be able to show her the woman was a fake, that she was reading something into nothing—I don't *know*.' He sank his face in his hands. 'But I agreed to go.'

Laura leaned forward, taking his hands.

'Then why did you change your mind?' she asked gently. 'It's important.'

He looked up at her; his face haggard with pain. 'Because Zara telephoned.'

'Zara?' She felt herself go white.

'That's right. She always kept in touch with Lydia. They wrote and telephoned constantly. But the morning she rang, Lydia was out. I spoke to her. She asked for Lydia, asked how she was. She appeared very concerned. And I told her what had happened. I didn't know her very well then, and I didn't like what I knew. But somehow when I spoke to her—well, it was a relief just to talk to someone who knew Lydia. I couldn't discuss it with John. I was desperate with worry. I told her about the Indian woman . . .' He paused. 'And she seemed very helpful. Very businesslike—efficient. She told me, quite definitely, not to go. She said it would make Lydia worse, that I should stay away from her. It was partly what I thought anyway. She was so reasonable, so plausible. So——' he spread his hands helplessly, 'I didn't go. I left for the location. It never occurred to me that she would take John. And Alex . . ..'

Laura stared at him silently. She thought of the Tarot cards; *Les Amoureux; La Mort*.

'Do you know,' she asked at last, 'why she wanted to take you?'

He met her eyes wretchedly. 'Yes,' he said slowly. 'I realised when it happened. I think she meant to kill me, and herself—

in the car.' He sighed. 'It was the only way she had left, you
see, of altering fate.'

'So the crash *was* deliberate? I thought so.' She met his gaze
sadly.

'But you see what this means? John died in my place. Alex
could have died. It was my fault.'

'No!' she cried fiercely. 'You mustn't think that! If it was
anyone's fault, it was Lydia's; she drove the car.' She paused.
'And perhaps not even Lydia's. Something more—something
else.' She hesitated, remembering the force of hatred she had
sensed that day in Zara. *Perhaps*, she thought.

She pressed his hands. 'Do you feel guilty for what
happened, Robert?'

'No,' he said steadily. 'I did, but not now.' He smiled, his
voice suddenly dry. 'Somehow, now, there isn't much room in
my heart for that.' He frowned. 'There was a hard time. A
kind of expiation, if you like.' He paused. 'And then I met
you.'

'I see.'

She looked away, and he turned her hands so they lay in his
upturned palms, tightly gripped.

'Do you, Laura?'

'I think so.' She lowered her head. 'I see why you asked me
to marry you. I had thought it was because of Alex, to keep
me here. But I see now—to make it come true. All those . . .
prophecies.'

To her surprise he burst out laughing, his laughter lighting
his whole face, startling her in the quiet of the room.

'Laura,' he said, 'you're such a sweet fool. Because I love
you.'

'You *love* me?' She stared at him.

'Yes, love you. You—no one else. Can't you understand
that?' He shook her roughly. 'Nothing to do with dreams and
prophecies and foreknowledge or any other mumbo-jumbo.
Because of what you *are*. I love you with my whole heart. I
know it more strongly than I've ever known anything in my
life—so much, so strongly, that it wouldn't surprise me if it
could be sensed on the other side of the universe, the galaxy.'

Laura looked at him in silence, wondering.

'Don't you see? It's such a force—when a man, a woman,
loves like that. Maybe poor Lydia did have some of the gifts
she claimed. Sometimes, in a house like this one——' he
looked up into the dark corners of the room, 'the past is

strong, almost palpable. Perhaps, for Lydia, the future was also . . .' He hesitated, then smiled mockingly. 'What I felt was certainly sensed by lots of other people—Graham, Cissie—I'm sure she knew, she dropped enough hints to me to sink a battleship. Alex, perhaps.' He paused. 'Zara.'

She met his eyes, and a look of understanding passed between them. 'Yes,' she said, 'I think Zara knew.'

'She hated you.' Robert said it flatly, both knowing it to be the truth. 'And hatred's a malevolent thing; a powerful thing. But not as powerful as love.' He looked at her seriously for a moment, and then the happiness he felt began slowly, irrepressibly to light his eyes again. 'In short,' he said drily, 'what I felt for you was only too apparent to everyone. Except you.'

'But of course,' she cried indignantly. 'You never said . . .'

'I never denied it,' he said steadily. 'Not even to Graham— if you'd listened carefully, and not leapt so quickly to conclusions . . .'

'But you said it was impossible—we didn't have a future— you said that.'

'Ah yes, I did.' He grinned. 'I'm cursed with a sense of responsibility, you see. After all, I'm so much older than you. And I had—indirectly—been the cause of suffering in the past. Unhappiness.' He paused. 'And so I thought you'd be better off without my attentions. With someone like Graham, perhaps.'

'You *were* jealous!'

'Not in the least,' he said smoothly. 'I could cheerfully have killed him, of course, that first day I saw you together. I'd been lying to myself a good deal up until then. After that— well, it became a little more difficult. Also——' he glanced at her sideways, 'I wanted you, very much—as you know quite well. More than I've ever wanted any woman in my life. It just took me a little while to admit the *ways* in which I wanted you. As my woman.' He reached out and touched her. 'As my love. As my wife.'

There was a long silence; he bent and kissed her lips, then he drew back, and they just sat, looking at one another.

'When . . .' Laura paused. She was going to ask a woman's question, she thought wryly, and she blushed.

'When did I know?' He smiled at her. 'Would you like me to say when I first saw you? That's the correct answer. I believe.'

'Tell me the truth.'

There was a silence. 'I knew in the desert,' he said at last. 'I saw then, with new eyes, all I'd sensed since I met you.'

'I knew then too. I didn't admit it to myself, but I knew.'

'My darling!' Robert gathered her into his arms. 'Perhaps we were both afraid.'

He kissed her then, for a long while, very gently, and when they drew apart he looked down happily into her eyes, trying to force his face into an expression of stern interrogation. And failing, she thought joyfully.

'So—who is this man you loved once, that you told me about last night?' he demanded fiercely.

'You. And your woman?'

'You.' He paused. 'I suppose I should confess at this point that my life up until now hasn't been entirely celibate . . .'

'I knew that!' She stared at him indignantly. 'I thought from the first you were an appallingly practised flirt. You flirted with me! Shamelessly.'

'Can you blame me?' He pulled her tight against him. 'But I've never lied, Laura. Not to any woman. I've never said what I've said to you, ever before. I always thought, you see, it would be a pity to devalue the words. When I used them . . . I wanted them to be right.'

'Say them again!' she cried impulsively. 'I know it's weak and I know it's stupid, but last time—I couldn't quite believe you . . .'

'I love you, Laura. And I always shall.' He laughed. 'It's very simple.'

She kissed him then, and he held her, moving his hands gently, with a fierce possessiveness, over her body. She closed her eyes, feeling the new knowledge he had given her surge instantly through her blood, parting her lips for him, drawing his hand down, there, to her breast. She kissed him then as she had always wanted to kiss him, without restraint or hesitancy, like a woman, not a girl, and she knew he sensed the change, that it aroused him. She murmured his name, like a soft incantation, drawing his hand under the thin silk of her blouse, and against the warm full curve of her breasts. Robert groaned, said something, his voice thick against her throat, and then, with difficulty, he drew back.

'You little witch,' he said softly. 'What are you doing to me now? Damn it, where did you learn?'

'From you.' She forced him to meet her gaze. 'Now, tell me—shall I leave, go, the way you said?'

'Are you attempting to persuade me, by any chance?'

'Yes.'

'And you called me shameless!' He laughed softly. 'No, you shan't go. You can't. And not . . .' he moved her hands firmly aside as she reached for him, 'not because you're attempting to hex me with your sexual wiles either, damn it. No.' He paused, his brow contracting a little. 'Because I feel—I don't know why—that you were right. You are . . . safe.'

'But of course.' She smiled at him gently. 'I love you.'

'And I love you.'

She laughed. 'You see? Invincible. Can't you feel it?'

His face grew serious. He took her hands and laid them against his, palm to palm.

'Yes,' he said gravely, 'I can.'

'Just now, do you think?' she added, suddenly afraid of their happiness.

'Oh no,' he said seriously. 'I think always. Don't you? Ever after.'

And with a quick gesture, taking her by surprise, as if he knew her answer and knew they had no need to speak it, he pulled her to her feet, and held her.

'So,' he said drily, looking into her eyes, 'that's settled, then. However, there's a great deal still to attend to. We must get married—immediately, don't you think? And then I want you to have my children. And I want to make love to you. Rather more thoroughly and in a more leisurely manner than I did so last night . . .'

'But I'm injured,' Laura reminded him. 'I've just been in an accident.'

'Too damn bad.' With a swift movement he lifted her into his arms. 'You can sleep in my bed tonight.'

'Sleep?'

'At intervals. But first . . .' he carried her to the door, 'we're going upstairs, and we're going to tell Alex.'

'But he's asleep,' she protested futilely as he carried her into the hall.

'I'll wake him up—very gently. He won't mind in the least. And besides, I want him to know. I want the world to know, actually, but Alex first.'

In fact there was no need to wake Alex. He stirred as they came softly into his room, and his eyes opened.

'Hello,' he said cheerfully, his voice blurry with sleep.

Robert hesitated, suddenly awkward.

'Alex,' he said gently.

'Yes, Uncle Robert?' He gave a large yawn.

'I wanted to tell you . . .' He broke off and glanced at
Laura, who was smiling. 'If it makes you feel any better,' he
hissed crossly at her, 'I now feel perfectly idiotic. I don't think
men are very good at this sort of thing.'

'No good at all.' Laura crossed to the bed, and tucked Alex
up. 'We're going to be married, Uncle Robert and I,' she said
gently. 'We love each other very much and . . .'

'I thought you did.' Alex gave another cavernous yawn and
turned over. 'Good,' he said sleepily.

'So if you need me, Alex, you'll know where I . . .'

'In Uncle Robert's room. Like last time.' He settled himself
against the pillow. Laura gently smoothed the sheets. His eyes
closed peacefully.

'I'll draw you a picture, Uncle Robert,' he said sleepily. 'A
wedding picture, with bells and things and Laura in a white
dress. Give it to you . . .' his voice trailed away, 'in the
morning . . .'

'Er—not too early, Alex.' Robert had retreated to the door.
Laura looked down. Alex was already asleep.

Outside, on the landing corridor, he took her hand, and
their eyes met; they laughed softly.

'A white dress?' Laura frowned ruefully. 'I shan't have the
right.'

'You wore your white dress last night.' He led her along the
corridor to his room and opened the door. 'In fact . . .' he gave
her the old sideways flirtatious glance, 'I'm not sure I didn't
intend to seduce you in that dress the very day I bought it.'

'You conceited creature!' She gave him a push. 'How did
you know I'd co-operate?'

'I told you once before, when I make up my mind about
something . . .' He drew her to the bed, and sat down, pulling her
to him, so he held her, standing, between his thighs, his arms
circling her waist, so she looked down directly into his face.

Then he took her hand with an odd, almost formal gesture.
'My darling. Content?'

'Yes.'

He smiled. 'Funny' so am I.'

There was a little silence; unbearable happiness, Laura
thought.

'Now,' said Robert, 'come here.' And he drew her down
beside him.

 **ROMANCE**

Next month's romances from Mills & Boon

Each month, you can choose from a world of variety in romance with Mills & Boon. These are the new titles to look out for next month.

ECSTASY Anne Weale
CARIBBEAN CONFUSION Mary Lyons
PACIFIC APHRODITE Madeleine Ker
A SPLENDID PASSION Avery Thorne
PROPHECY OF DESIRE Claire Harrison
THE FAILED MARRIAGE Carole Mortimer
HOUSE OF MEMORIES Margaret Way
WILDTRACK Nicola West
THE ASHBY AFFAIR Lynsey Stevens
TAKE IT OR LEAVE IT Elizabeth Oldfield
RELUCTANT RELATIVE Jessica Steele
A MODERN GIRL Rebecca Flanders

Buy them from your usual paperback stockist, or write to: Mills & Boon Reader Service, P.O. Box 236, Thornton Rd, Croydon, Surrey CR9 3RU, England. Readers in South Africa-write to: Mills & Boon Reader Service of Southern Africa, Private Bag X3010, Randburg, 2125.

Mills & Boon
the rose of romance

Doctor Nurse Romances

Romance in the wide world of medicine

Amongst the intense emotional pressures of modern medical life, doctors and nurses often find romance. Read about their lives and loves in the four fascinating Doctor Nurse romances, available this month.

THE RETURN OF DR BORIS
Lisa Cooper

DOCTOR IN NEW GUINEA
Dana James

PARIS NURSE
Margaret Barker

ROSES FOR CHRISTMAS
Betty Neels

Mills & Boon
the rose of romance

An orchestra for you

In the Rose of Romance Orchestra, conducted by Jack Dorsey of '101 Strings' fame, top musicians have been brought together especially to reproduce in music the moods and sounds of Romance.

The Rose of Romance Orchestra brings you classic romantic songs like Yours, Just the Way You Are, September Song and many others.

We promise you a new dimension of pleasure and enjoyment as you read your favourite romances from Mills & Boon.

Volumes 1 & 2 now available on the Rose Records label wherever good records are bought.

Usual price £3.99 (Record or Cassette)

VOLUME TWO

VOLUME ONE

THE ROSE OF ROMANCE ORCHESTRA

Yours·Theme from Dr. Zhivago·Romeo & Juliet·You Don't Bring Me Flowers
Just The Way You Are·Cavatina·Can't Smile Without You·September Song
Days Of Wine & Roses·Send In The Clowns·Shadow Of Your Smile·All By Myself

Mills & Boon

The rose of romance.

YOURS absolutely FREE
Mills & Boon Catalogue

We know you enjoyed this Mills & Boon Romance. So we'd like to tell you all about the whole range of other exciting titles we offer — titles we know you wouldn't want to miss!

The Mills & Boon Catalogue offers you a fantastic selection of Romantic fiction written by the world's leading authors. Longer Romances offering you nearly four hundred pages of passion and intrigue. Dr/Nurse Romances for a truly romantic look at the world of medicine and our Masquerade Series to whisk you away to bygone ages. There is also a selection from our Romance Series, PLUS a whole range of exciting bargain book offers!

What are you waiting for? For your FREE Mills & Boon Catalogue simply complete and send the coupon to:— MILLS & BOON READER SERVICE, P.O. BOX 236, THORNTON ROAD, CROYDON, SURREY, CR9 3RU, ENGLAND. OR why not telephone us on 01-684 2141 and we will send you your catalogue by return of post.

Please note:— **READERS IN SOUTH AFRICA** write to Mills & Boon Ltd., Postbag X3010, Randburg 2125, S. Africa.